DANDELION	DOG-ROSE	

p46	p50	p52

FOXGLOVE	GERMANDER SPEEDWELL	GORSE

p56	p60	p62

GREATER STITCHWORT	HAREBELL	HEDGE BINDWEED

p64	p66	p68

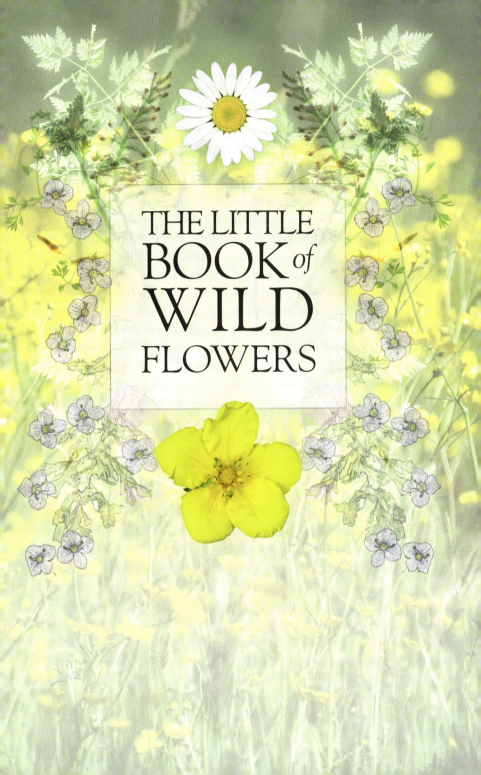
THE LITTLE BOOK of WILD FLOWERS

First published in 2021 by Fine Feather Press Limited
The Coach House, Elstead Road, Farnham, Surrey GU10 1JE
Copyright © 2021 Fine Feather Press Limited

All rights reserved. No part of this publication may be reproduced, stored in a retrieval system or transmitted in any form or by any means, electronic, mechanical, photocopying, recording or otherwise, without the prior permission of the publishers.

2 4 6 8 10 9 7 5 3 1

A CIP catalogue record is available from the British Library
ISBN: 978-1-908489-44-9
Printed in China

Fine Feather Press Ltd makes every effort to ensure that the papers used in its books are made from trees that have been legally sourced from well-managed and credibly certified forests.

www.finefeatherpress.com

THE LITTLE BOOK of WILD FLOWERS

A NEW WORLD TO DISCOVER

Consultant: Dr Trevor Dines

Contents

Foreword	7	Cow parsley	36
Bluebell	8	Other umbellifers	38
Bramble	10	Cowslip	40
Bugle	12	Cuckooflower	42
Coastal flowers	14	Daisy	44
Common bird's-foot-trefoil	16	Dandelion	46
		Other daisies	48
Other peas & vetches	18	Dog-rose	50
		Field scabious	52
Common comfrey	20	Flower gallery	54
Common dog-violet	22	Foxglove	56
		Fruit gallery	58
Common knapweed	24	Germander speedwell	60
Common poppy	26	Gorse	62
Common ragwort	28	Greater stitchwort	64
Common spotted-orchid	30	Harebell	66
		Hedge bindweed	68
Other orchids	32	Herb-Robert	70
Cornflower	34	Herb gallery	72

Honeysuckle	74	Rosebay	
Insects	76	willowherb	112
Invasive species	78	Scarlet pimpernel	114
Ivy	80	Seed dispersal	116
Lady's bedstraw	82	Snowdrop	118
Leaf gallery	84	Stinging nettle	120
Lesser celandine	86	Tormentil	122
Marsh thistle	88	Wetland plant	
Meadow buttercup	90	gallery	124
Meadows	92	Wildlife corridors	126
Meadowsweet	94	Wild strawberry	128
Parasitic plants	96	Wild teasel	130
Pollination	98	Wood anemone	132
Primrose	100	Wood forget-	134
Ragged-Robin	102	me-not	
Ramsons	104	Yarrow	136
Red campion	106	Yellow iris	138
Red clover	108	Glossary	140
Red dead-nettle	110	Index	142
	Acknowledgements	144	

Foreword

BY DR TREVOR DINES OF PLANTLIFE

Whether it is a daisy on a lawn, a cowslip on a verge, or even an orchid on a woodland walk, you are never far from wild flowers. They are all around us – splashes of colour in our daily lives – yet they often go nameless and remain unfamiliar. This fabulous little book will help you to identify over 50 wild flowers, bringing them to life with amazing facts about their ecology and folklore.

Plants are incredible friends. They capture energy from the sun and use this to provide life support for all our wildlife. Though seemingly fragile, they are the Earth's most effective way of capturing carbon and preventing flooding and soil erosion. They provide us with oxygen to breathe, medicines to heal and food to eat, and they colour our landscapes and bring us immense joy.

My passion began when I found an orchid on the farm where I grew up. I hope this book ignites similar curiosity and encourages you to make friends with the flowers at your feet.

FACTFILE

FOUND: Woods, shady banks, cliff-tops
SIZE: Up to 50 cm
FLOWERS: Apr to Jun
PETALS: 6
SHAPE: Flower clusters on leafless stems
FAMILY: Asparagus

Bluebell
Hyacinthoides non-scripta

IN SHADY PLACES the bluebell lies – not on its own, but in crowds of hundreds or thousands. Few wild flowers cover the ground so completely or smell as sweet, and the sight is one of the wonders of spring. Along with primroses, ramsons and wood anemones, they are a sign that you are in ancient woodland.

The nodding flowers open from the bottom, with between five and 20 heads on each stem. Some believe that you may be led astray by fairies if you pick them. Whether or not this is true, they wilt quickly, are poisonous and produce lots of slimy juice, not to mention the fact that picking them is against the law.

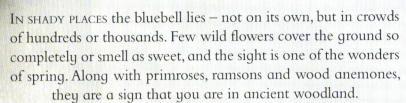

POLLINATORS
Bees push into the flowers to feed on the sweet nectar inside. In doing so, they brush against the white pollen on the male stamens, carrying it away to pollinate other flowers.

SPOT THE DIFFERENCE
You may stumble across mauve, pink or even white bluebells, like the one shown on the right below. The ones on the left are Spanish bluebells, which also flower in April and May. Compared with our native bluebell, Spanish ones have wider flowers which grow all around the stem, not just to one side. They are also bigger and more upright with lighter-blue flowers and no smell.

Bramble
Rubus fruticosus

The delicately coloured, slightly crumpled flowers of the bramble are a common sight from spring to late summer. The name bramble or blackberry actually refers to hundreds of microspecies which are all very slightly different from one another and which can produce seeds without being fertilised.

One of the first people known to have eaten blackberries was Haraldskær Woman. She lived over 2,500 years ago and her preserved remains were found in a bog in Denmark in 1835 with traces of the fruit in her stomach.

WILDLIFE
Insects, like this silver-washed fritillary, feed on the nectar produced by bramble flowers. Later in the year, birds and mammals gorge on the deep purple berries, helping to spread the seeds far and wide in their droppings.

USES
Every part of the bramble plant has been used by humans – for treating health problems such as bleeding gums; for dyeing cloth; and for making pies, jellies, jams and cordials.

BRAMBLE JAM
Gently dissolve 350g of preserving sugar in 350g blackberries mixed with the juice of one lemon. Boil the mixture for 15 minutes, then put a small amount on a cold plate. If wrinkles appear, the jam is ready and it can be put into clean jars.

FACTFILE
FOUND: Hedgerows, woods, scrub, heaths
SIZE: 1 to 3 m
FLOWERS: Jun to Sep
PETALS: 5
SHAPE: Bushy plants with thorny stems
FAMILY: Rose

BUGLE
Ajuga reptans

IF A FLASH OF BLUE catches your eye in the woods in spring, it may be a bugle reaching up towards the light from its shady abode. Some flowers droop on floppy stems, but the bugle stands straight upright. Its square stem has two hairy and two smooth sides, with layers of leaves and flowers packed in against it.

The *reptans* part of its scientific name means "creeping" in Latin. This refers to the shoots it sends out along the ground, which put down roots to form new plants. Bugle was popular as a remedy to calm nerves, cure coughs and to stop bleeding.

POLLINATORS
Many insects rely on bugle's sweet nectar as an early source of food in the spring, particularly bees, butterflies and moths. As the insects gather the nectar, they move pollen grains from the male to the female parts of the flowers, thereby fertilising them.

FLOWERS
Amid the glossy leaves are layers of small, violet-blue flowers. They look like human paper-chain decorations with arms held out wide. You may be lucky enough to find bugle with flowers that are pink or white, but these are not very common.

GROUND-IVY
It is easy to confuse bugle and ground-ivy for they look similar and both flower in the spring in shady places. Check the leaves – those of ground-ivy (below) are rounder, with longer stalks and toothed edges.

FACTFILE
FOUND: Shady, damp woods & grassland
SIZE: Up to 30 cm
FLOWERS: Apr to Jun
PETALS: 2, deeply lobed
SHAPE: Low-growing with flowering spires
FAMILY: Mint

COASTAL FLOWERS

SHRUBBY SEA-BLITE, small adder's-tongue and biting stonecrop – these strange names belong to some of our wonderful coastal wild flowers. Some thrive on sandy dunes and beaches, while others have adapted to living along muddy estuaries or on rocky cliffs and shores. What they all have in common is the need to withstand the coast's often harsh weather conditions such as strong winds and salty air.

Opposite is a mound of thrift. It grows close to the ground out of the wind and its thin leaves help to prevent excess water loss, for the rocks, cliffs and beaches where it grows are bare and dry. Unlike thrift's narrow leaves, some other coastal plants have waxy, shiny or hairy ones. These are all different ways of helping the plants to trap the water they need to survive.

COMMON BIRD'S-FOOT-TREFOIL
Lotus corniculatus

THIS CHEERING YELLOW FLOWER lights up our grasslands over the summer months. Carpets form in meadows and on scrubby banks, which are soon alive with bumblebees and butterflies flitting between flowers. Yet common bird's-foot-trefoil doesn't give its food up easily. The insects have to push apart the two lower wing petals to reach the sweet nectar inside.

Although humans eat the seeds from many plants in the pea family, common bird's-foot-trefoil isn't one of these. Yet it is grown as a crop to feed cattle and sheep and to help farmers improve the quality of their soil.

BUTTERFLIES
Common blue butterflies love this plant. The female flutters around looking for the tenderest young leaves on which to lay her eggs. It is also the main food and larval plant for dingy skippers, silver-studded blues and wood white butterflies.

WHAT'S IN A NAME?
Bird's-foot, granny's toenails, devil's claws – this wild flower has picked up some strange names along the way. All these stem from the shape of the ripe seed pods which you can see below. The hooks at the tips make the pods look strangely like claws – more like a bird's talons, one hopes, than granny's nails. Another popular name is eggs and bacon – eggs for the yolk-yellow petals and bacon for the amber buds.

FACTFILE
FOUND: Meadows, banks, heaths, cliffs
SIZE: Up to 40 cm
FLOWERS: May to Sep
PETALS: 5
SHAPE: Sprawling, low-growing plant
FAMILY: Pea

OTHER PEAS & VETCHES

POLLINATED FLOWERS from this family form long pods with seeds. Many, such as peas and beans, have been eaten by humans and livestock for thousands of years. Here are some of the most common pea and vetch species to look out for – but there are many others with the same distinctive arrangement of petals.

EVERLASTING-PEA

TUFTED VETCH

BROOM
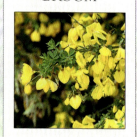

GOAT'S-RUE

KIDNEY VETCH

COMMON VETCH

SAINFOIN

MEADOW VETCHLING
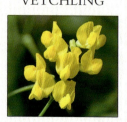

COMMON RESTHARROW

A CLOSER LOOK at BITTER-VETCH

Pea-family flowers share the same basic shape, with an upright top petal called a standard, two wing petals and a lower lip or keel made from two fused petals.

FACTFILE
FOUND: Rivers, fens, ditches, waste ground
SIZE: Up to 1.2 m
FLOWERS: Apr to Jul
PETALS: 5
SHAPE: Tubular flowers on tall hairy stems
FAMILY: Borage

Common Comfrey
Symphytum officinale

The delicate flowers of common comfrey seem very small among its mass of green leaves. If you brush your hand against the foliage, it will feel rough like sandpaper because of the tiny hooked hairs that line both the leaves and stems.

The plant has strong binding properties, hence the *sympho* part of comfrey's scientific name, which means "to join". Historically, the roots were applied directly to cuts and grazes and used to mend broken bones. Today, some gardeners grow comfrey in order to make use of its leaves which, when mixed with water, make a powerful fertiliser for garden plants.

FLOWERS

Members of the comfrey family have drooping clusters of bell-like flowers which form in pairs. Before the buds open, they are curled in a spiral like a scorpion's tail as the picture below shows. Common comfrey flowers from April to July.

THE BORAGE FAMILY

You may recognise some other borage family members, if not the names. Green alkanet (below left) is easy to remember because the flowers are … blue! Its name comes from the fact that its leaves stay green throughout the year, with flowers appearing from March to July.

Lungwort (below right) is also common in spring. The leaf spots are formed by pockets of air, making them look like lungs. It was believed that this would make them effective in treating chest infections.

COMMON DOG-VIOLET
Viola riviniana

THESE LOW-LYING PURPLE FLOWERS are some of the first to appear in the early days of spring. Many other wild-flower names also feature animals such as harebell, cat's-ear, goat's-beard and foxglove. "Dog" here is not used in a kindly way, referring to its lack of scent – unlike its sweet violet cousin.

There are about 800 species of violet in the world but this is the one most commonly found growing wild in the UK. Like goldilocks, it likes its surroundings to be not too shady but not too sunny; not too dry but not too damp. The young leaves can be used to make tea or to thicken soups.

WILDLIFE
Bees push their way deep into the flowers to reach the nectar, while slugs may nibble directly through the back of the flowers. Dog-violets are also an important food source for the caterpillars of some fritillary butterflies.

FLOWERS AND LEAVES
These curiously shaped flowers are made up of five purple petals fringed with five pointed green sepals, with stems growing up from a tuft of heart-shaped leaves.

Seeds form in a capsule in the slipper-shaped spur which sticks out from the back of the flower. When ripe, the capsule splits and hurls the seeds away. Ants may then carry them further still, to dine on their oily coating.

FACTFILE

FOUND: Hedgerows, woods, grassland
SIZE: Up to 20 cm
FLOWERS: Apr to Jun
PETALS: 5
SHAPE: Low clumps with short leafy stems
FAMILY: Violet

FACTFILE
FOUND: Verges, rough grassy areas
SIZE: Up to 1 m
FLOWERS: Jun to Sep
PETALS: Many
SHAPE: Stiff stems with single flowerheads
FAMILY: Daisy

COMMON KNAPWEED
Centaurea nigra

THE TUFTY HEADS OF COMMON KNAPWEED add spots of colour to scrubby grassland throughout the summer. It looks like a type of thistle, but it lacks the tell-tale prickles. This knapweed can be identified by the dark knobbly head at the top of every stem from which the crown of reddish-purple flowers emerges.

This is a tough wild flower which thrives in rough ground and is quite hard to get rid of once established. Some view it as a weed, but it is a rich source of nectar and an effective way of attracting pollinating insects to nearby crops. Knapweed flowers are edible and make a pretty addition to summer salads.

GREATER KNAPWEED
This close cousin prefers a lime-rich soil and is less widespread. Its flowers are more showy than common knapweed, and the ball of overlapping leafy scales below each flowerhead is paler, with fringed tips.

PARASITE
Below is knapweed broomrape. It lacks the green pigment that helps plants to make food. This is because it is a parasite, attaching itself to knapweed roots and robbing them of food and water.

WILDLIFE
Common knapweed's rich nectar stores make its flowers a hot spot for insects, such as the capsid bugs below. In the autumn, charms of goldfinches and other seed-eating birds gorge on the downy seedheads.

Common Poppy
Papaver rhoeas

Over 6,000 years ago, farmers migrating from southern to northern Europe brought poppy seeds mixed in with their corn. Today, the flowers still emerge each year, all crinkled from their drooping buds, to live for one glorious day. The petals are the purest red and tissue thin, some with spots of black at their base.

The common or corn poppy develops from seed each year in areas of disturbed ground where there is enough light, such as farmed fields. This is why they grew in the churned-up battlefields of the First World War, which has led to their being a symbol of remembrance for those that died.

YELLOW POPPIES

In addition to five species of red poppy, we have two yellow ones as well. The Welsh poppy (shown on the left) prefers damp shady places, unlike its sun-loving common-poppy relative. The other is the yellow horned-poppy – a sunny splash of colour on shingle beaches – which is so named for its long, curving horn-like seed pods. The stem gives out a yellow sap when cut, which is extremely poisonous and so is obviously best avoided.

CAPSULES

Common poppies can be identified by the shape of their seed capsules – smooth and oval with striped rays – and by the hairs that grow at right angles to their slender stems, as you can see clearly in this picture.

FACTFILE

FOUND: Farmland, waste ground, verges
SIZE: Up to 60 cms
FLOWERS: Jun to Aug
PETALS: 4
SHAPE: Large, single flowers on slim stems
FAMILY: Poppy

COMMON RAGWORT
Senecio jacobaea

LOVED BY SOME and hated by others, this is a key plant for insects. Well over 100 species – some scarce – feed on its bountiful nectar stores, while yet more dine on its leaves. The ragwort displays a mass of golden flowers which continue to bloom well into October when most other insect food has disappeared.

Owners of cattle and horses are less enthusiastic about what is officially a weed, for its leaves and flowers contain a poisonous substance called jacobine. Eating sufficient quantities can cause long-term liver damage and even death in livestock, although animals tend to avoid it if other food is available.

OTHER RAGWORTS
Marsh, hoary, fen and broad-leaved – there is a ragwort species for almost every environment. Oxford ragwort, which you can see below, flowers from March and forms smaller, bushier clumps than common ragwort.

CINNABAR MOTHS
Where there is ragwort growing, there are likely to be cinnabar-moth caterpillars, for this is the only plant that they feed on. Their bright stripes warn birds that they are poisonous, and only the cuckoo is able to digest them.

LEAVES
Standing up to 1.5 metres tall, this wild flower has jagged dark green leaves running alternately up the stem. These give the plant an air of being rather shabby, especially as the lower ones have often withered and died by the time the plant flowers.

FACTFILE
FOUND: Verges, rough grassy areas
SIZE: Up to 1.5 m
FLOWERS: Jun to Oct
PETALS: Many
SHAPE: Branched stems with flower clusters
FAMILY: Daisy

COMMON SPOTTED-ORCHID

Dactylorhiza fuchsii

ORCHIDS HAVE A CAPTIVATING appeal for many people: they are exotic, and to discover one is thrilling. This species is the most common European orchid and although it is not too difficult to find, it may be tricky to identify. It readily cross-breeds with other orchids, making plants that can be tall, short, spotted or unspotted, and range in colour from pink or purple to white.

The scientific name *dactylorhiza* comes from the Ancient Greek meaning "finger-shaped roots", which is what its fleshy tubers resemble. *Fuchsii* honours the 16th-century German-born Leonhart Fuchs, who was an important early botanist.

A CLOSER LOOK

From early summer, floral spikes rise up from the ground, set about with buds. Each fertilised flower produces thousands of tiny seeds which are then carried away on the wind. Their journey isn't easy, for they need to land in soil where a particular fungus lives – this supplies the seeds with the food they need to grow. Three or four years later, the plants are ready, finally, to produce flowers.

LEAVES

Long, strap-like leaves wrap themselves around the base of the stem, and smaller leaves cling to the stalk. To determine whether you are looking at a common spotted-orchid, check to see if it has short and long dashes. Small, scattered spots are more likely to mean it's a heath orchid.

FACTFILE
FOUND: Meadows, woods, verges
SIZE: Up to 70 cm
FLOWERS: Jun to Aug
PETALS: 3
SHAPE: Single stalks ending in flower spikes
FAMILY: Orchid

Other orchids

Most of the world's orchids are found in tropical regions, but we have some surprisingly exotic species of our own, many of which are endangered. They make up the largest family of flowering plants with about 26,000 species, most notable for the shape of their lower lip petal, as the bee orchid typifies.

EARLY-PURPLE ORCHID

Look for clusters of purple flowers in woods and grassy areas from April to June. This orchid's long spotted leaves and unpleasant smell help to identify it.

AUTUMN LADY'S-TRESSES

These small flowers spiral around each stem like hair braids. This is the last orchid to flower in the year, appearing in areas of short grass from August to September.

PYRAMIDAL ORCHID

From June to August, these pink pyramids rise up out of chalky grasslands. The flowers and leaves are plain, unlike those of some similar-looking orchids.

A CLOSER LOOK at a BEE ORCHID

This spectacular orchid grows on chalky grasslands and verges from June to late July. The flower's shape, pattern and scent mimic a female bee in order to lure male bees in to pollinate it.

Cornflower
Centaurea cyanus

Fields were once filled with cornflowers growing in among the crops. They were a wonderful sight, but an annoying tough-stemmed weed for farmers. Then came the use of herbicides (weedkillers), and cornflower numbers dropped so drastically that they almost died out completely in the UK. Nowadays, truly wild cornflowers here are rare, and many that you see on waysides have been sown as part of wild-flower seed mixes.

In days gone by, cornflowers were used as a calming treatment for eye infections among other ailments, and the juice would be extracted from the brilliant blue petals for making ink.

POLLINATORS
Plants have many ways of saying "come visit me" to passing insects in the hope of being pollinated. The cornflower's outer crown of trumpet-shaped flowers is there for just this purpose – seen here enticing an ant and a butterfly.

COLOURS
Fuchsias, violets, poppies and cornflowers all give their names to particular colours. The intense blue of the cornflower fades as the petals wither. Some lighter, almost lilac-pink variations can be found, as well as the occasional white one.

GATHERING RIPE SEEDS
Cornflowers are annuals which means they grow, flower, set seed and die all within one year. To gather the seeds, tease the seedhead (shown below) apart and leave the individual seeds to dry for a couple of days before storing.

FACTFILE
FOUND: Verges, waste ground, cornfields
SIZE: Up to 90 cm
FLOWERS: Jun to Aug
PETALS: Many
SHAPE: Single flower heads on slender stalks
FAMILY: Daisy

FACTFILE
FOUND: Hedgerows, verges, wood edges
SIZE: Up to 1.5 m
FLOWERS: Apr to Jun
PETALS: Many
SHAPE: Tall, branching heads of white flowers
FAMILY: Carrot

COW PARSLEY
Anthriscus sylvestris

YOU MAY OR MAY NOT look like the other members of your family. Cow parsley most definitely does. It belongs to a group of flowering plants known as the carrot family, or umbellifers, many of which have similar clusters of delicate white flowers.

Cow parsley is the first to appear in the spring, filling hedgerows with clouds of creamy-white flowers. It is followed by other umbellifers such as rough chervil, upright hedge-parsley and hogweed. In certain areas, children used to be told that their mothers would die if they brought cow parsley inside – to stop them picking the similar, but poisonous, hemlock by mistake.

WILDLIFE
Rich in nectar, cow parsley attracts many insects but especially flies, hoverflies and bees. In the winter, insects make use of the plant's hollow stems for shelter – you could try bundling some together to make a bug hotel.

A CLOSER LOOK
In the dark days of February, you may find the fresh green leaves of cow parsley beginning to emerge – these are long, pointed and fern-like. The flowers give way to teardrop-shaped seeds, while the hollow ribbed flower stems turn from green to purple as they age. These make excellent pea-shooters, but this is not advised owing to the plant's likeness to hemlock, as mentioned above.

OTHER UMBELLIFERS

UMBELLIFERS ARE ANOTHER NAME for members of the carrot family. Umbels are the flower clusters that form from stalks, which look like the spokes of an umbrella. Some umbellifers are edible, such as carrots, parsnips and parsley, but some are incredibly toxic and can be fatal if eaten, such as hemlock.

ALEXANDERS

WILD CARROT

ROCK SAMPHIRE

GIANT HOGWEED

WILD PARSNIP

GROUND-ELDER

SANICLE
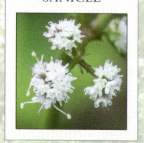

PIGNUT

SEA-HOLLY

COWSLIP
Primula veris

LOOK FOR THE SUN-YELLOW FLOWERS of the cowslip swaying in the breeze on sunny banks, on verges and in meadows. The cup-shaped flowers hang down to one side of the stem as though slightly sad or ashamed. Cowslips were once scarce because of a loss of habitat but their numbers are now increasing.

The name cowslip may have come from the word cowslop – an old word for cowpat, often found in the meadows where the cowslips grew. All parts of the plant have been used to create herbal remedies as well as a golden, sleep-inducing wine made from a mixture of the flowers with water, sugar and yeast.

WILDLIFE
Insects, especially honey bees and bumblebees, are drawn in by the orange markings at the base of each petal, leading them to the sweet nectar inside. The rarely seen Duke of Burgundy butterfly lays its eggs on the underside of cowslip leaves.

SEEDS AND LEAVES
After pollination, seeds form and ripen and are then scattered by the wind. Most fall near the parent plant, which is why you see great drifts of these flowers together. At the foot of each stem lies a circle of wrinkled green leaves.

FALSE OXLIP
The primrose – the cowslip's paler yellow cousin – flowers earlier in the spring in shadier spots. These two species sometimes interbreed to produce false oxlips. These are very similar to cowslips, but the flowers point in all directions, not just to one side.

FACTFILE
FOUND: Meadows, verges, banks, scrub
SIZE: Up to 30 cm
FLOWERS: Apr to May
PETALS: 5
SHAPE: Clusters of flowers on tall stems
FAMILY: Primrose

CUCKOOFLOWER
Cardamine pratensis

THE SOUND OF THE FIRST CUCKOO in spring marks the time when this flower appears, hence its name. It is also known as lady's smock and is found in wet grassy areas such as damp meadows, verges and river edges. It was once thought unlucky to bring it indoors, which may be why in some areas it is so common now.

The single stalk is very straight and ends with a cluster of lilac flowers – pale pink in shady areas and darker purple in sunnier spots. Once the flowers have been pollinated by insects, they form long seed pods. These curve upwards and slowly ripen until they explode to release the seeds inside.

BUTTERFLIES
As delicate as the flowers themselves are the orange-tip and green-veined white butterflies which feed and lay their eggs on them. The green colour of their caterpillars camouflages them against the seed pods and the leaves on which they feed.

GARLIC MUSTARD
Members of the cabbage or brassica family, such as the cuckooflower, have four petals arranged in a cross. Garlic mustard, shown below, is another example and is often found in places where the cuckooflower grows.

LEAVES
These leaves are richer in vitamin C than a lemon and are sometimes added to salads, although they do taste rather bitter. The leaves closest to the ground (shown right) are rounder than those further up the plant's stem (on the left).

FACTFILE
FOUND: Damp woods, meadows, verges
SIZE: Up to 60 cm
FLOWERS: Apr to Jun
PETALS: 4
SHAPE: Flower clusters on straight stems
FAMILY: Cabbage

Daisy
Bellis perennis

THERE IS A PROVERB that says summer is here when you can stand on seven daisies. This seems slightly fanciful as daisies flower for most of the year and are often at their best in spring. The name daisy is thought to come from "day's eye" because the flowerheads open in the sun and close up at night – an action common in the daisy family and known as nyctinasty.

In Ancient Rome, and elsewhere since then, surgeons have used daisy juice to heal soldiers' wounds. It is also whispered that fairies use daisies as a medicine to stop children from growing.

DAISY CHAINS

Wild flowers are best enjoyed where they grow. However, daisies are plentiful and are fun to pick for making daisy chains. Use your thumbnail to create a hole in the stem of one daisy and then thread the stem of another daisy through it. Short chains for bracelets, long chains for necklaces.

FLOWERS AND LEAVES

What looks like one flower is, in fact, very many tiny flowers. These are made up of two types – yellow central disc florets and white ray florets around the outside. During the day, daisies turn their heads towards the sun. This helps to warm the flowers and so to attract insects.

The flower stems are leafless but at their base lie flat circles of teaspoon-shaped leaves. By pressing against the earth, they avoid the blades of passing lawnmowers. Young leaves may be used in salads but tend to have a bitter taste which even cattle find unpleasant.

FACTFILE

FOUND: Lawns, grazed pastures
SIZE: Up to 12 cm
FLOWERS: Feb to Nov
PETALS: Many
SHAPE: Low clumps of flowers on single stems
FAMILY: Daisy

DANDELION
Taraxacum officinale

Hardly a month goes by without dandelion flowers being visible. If you look closely, you will see that their ragged yellow heads are made up of 150 or so tiny flowers. These sit on top of a leafless hollow stem which, if broken, oozes a milky sap.

Dandelion comes from the French *dents-de-lion* meaning "lion's teeth", referring to the jagged fang-like edges of the leaves. Picked young, these can be eaten in salads, while the flowers make an interesting beer or wine. Most useful of all is the long, black root which, roasted and ground, makes a type of coffee.

WILDLIFE
Horses, cattle and sheep find dandelions too bitter to eat, but rabbits and goats have no objections. Dandelions flower for much of the year, providing nectar and pollen for insects when other food sources are no longer available.

WHAT'S THE TIME?
Each floret produces a single seed ending in a slender spike and a plume of white hair. Together, they form a downy seedhead known as a clock. This comes from the belief that the hour of the day is the number of puffs it takes to blow the seeds away.

IS IT A DANDELION?
The name dandelion actually refers to over 200 wild flowers, which are all slightly different from one another and extremely hard to tell apart. Just to confuse matters, there are many other plants that look like dandelions, such as this hawkbit.

FACTFILE
FOUND: Gardens, grassy fields, verges
SIZE: Up to 20 cm
FLOWERS: Feb to Nov
PETALS: Many
SHAPE: Flower clumps on leafless stems
FAMILY: Daisy

OTHER DAISIES

THERE ARE OVER 22,000 SPECIES of daisy in the world, making it one of the largest of all flowering plant families. It includes familiar names such as thistle, dandelion and cornflower – not many of which look like the common daisy – which all have flowerheads made up of many flowers or florets.

SCENTLESS MAYWEED

SPEAR THISTLE

TANSY
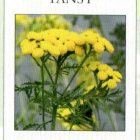

LESSER BURDOCK

GOAT'S-BEARD

HEMP-AGRIMONY

PINEAPPLEWEED

GROUNDSEL

NIPPLEWORT

A CLOSER LOOK at OXEYE DAISIES

Oxeye daisies have two types of floret making up each flowerhead – white ray florets to attract insects and yellow disc florets containing the male and female flower parts.

FACTFILE
FOUND: Woods, hedges, verges
SIZE: Up to 4 m
FLOWERS: Jun to Jul
PETALS: 5
SHAPE: Arching stems with hooked thorns
FAMILY: Rose

DOG-ROSE
Rosa canina

THIS IS OUR MOST COMMON wild rose. Its strongly arched stems, armed with hooked prickles, clamber through hedgerows and trees, seeking out the sun. The term dog-rose actually refers to a number of different species, which is why the colour of the flowers often varies from plant to plant and may be any shade between white and dark pink. Unlike the heavy perfume of some cultivated garden roses, the scent of dog-roses is delicate.

Roses have been used as a sign of secrecy over the centuries. When hung above a table or door, a rose would mean that whatever was discussed could not be repeated elsewhere.

GALLS
Spiky growths or galls, like the one below, are made by gall wasps. The female lays up to 60 eggs in a single leaf bud. The grubs then hatch out, creating these galls as they grow. It was once thought that burning the galls and applying the ashes to a man's head would cure baldness.

INSECTS
Beetles and bees crawl over the stamens at the centre of the flowers, collecting protein-filled pollen as they go. You won't see butterflies on dog-roses because they feed only on nectar, which is not produced by these flowers.

ROSE-HIP SYRUP
The seeds ripen in shiny oval cases called rose hips, which swell and turn red in the autumn. The hips are full of Vitamin C and make delicious syrups, jellies and jams when boiled with water and sugar.

FACTFILE
FOUND: Dry, chalky grassland and banks
SIZE: Up to 1 m
FLOWERS: Jun to Sep
PETALS: 4
SHAPE: Flat heads on long slender stems
FAMILY: Teasel

Field Scabious
Knautia arvensis

If you had sores in the Middle Ages, such as those caused by the plague, then you might have been given juice made from crushed field-scabious leaves. This attractive plant grows in dry chalky grassland, in meadows and along verges, and flowers during the summer months. The leaves lie at the base of the plant from which the pale lilac flowers rise up on slender stems.

The flowerheads look like perfect pincushions and range in colour from pale pink to lilac. Each head is actually a mass of up to 50 tiny flowers, each with four unequal petals. Those around the outside are larger and form a soft frill.

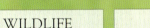

WILDLIFE

This striking six-spot burnet moth is not the only insect to feed on field scabious. Its nectar is also an important food for skippers, red admirals and fritillary butterflies, especially in late summer when nectar is hard to find.

OTHER SCABIOUS FLOWERS

If you see a flower that looks like field scabious, count the number of lobes on each of the florets. If there are five, then it is a small scabious. It produces dry ridged seed capsules (below right), which fall to the ground or catch on animals, to be transported away. Devil's-bit scabious (below left) has a rounder and darker purple flowerhead and grows in marshy areas.

FLOWER GALLERY

FLOWERS ARE THE SHOWY parts of plants and provide the easiest way to identify them. Typically, each flowerhead contains the male and female reproductive organs surrounded by a ring of petals. Around these are the smaller sepals, which protect the flower when it is in bud and which are often green.

The petals are usually brightly coloured to attract insects, which then carry pollen from the male to the female flower parts. Once pollinated, the fertilised flowers go on to produce seeds which may then form new plants. The wonder of the flower world is that they come in all shapes, colours and sizes. Here is a guide to some of the most common flower shapes.

HONESTY

Honesty is known as a crucifer. This is the term for flowers that have four petals in the shape of a cross.

MEADOW CRANE'S-BILL

The five petals of many wild flowers in the crane's-bill family curve gently upwards in a bowl shape.

COMMON POPPY

Paper-thin and crimson red, these saucer-shaped poppy flowers are flatter than those of meadow crane's-bill.

COMMON CENTAURY

These pink centaury flowers have very distinct petals which radiate out from the centre like a star.

LILY-OF-THE-VALLEY

In spring, the small white flowers of lily-of-the-valley hang down like little bells amid a sea of green leaves.

HEDGE BINDWEED

Twining around other plants, this pretty garden menace proclaims its presence with its trumpet-shaped flowers.

YELLOW ARCHANGEL

Some wild flowers have hooded or helmeted upper petals like this one. The angel shape is reflected in its name.

COMMON FUMITORY

Common fumitory flowers are tubular, and the upper petal is curved at the base to form a spur which holds nectar.

CORN MARIGOLD

Ligulate means having strap-like outer flowers, like this marigold. The whole flowerhead is made up of small florets.

FACTFILE
FOUND: Heaths, woods, hedges, embankments
SIZE: Up to 2 m
FLOWERS: Jun to Jul
PETALS: 5 fused
SHAPE: Tall spires of flowers on single stems
FAMILY: Speedwell

FOXGLOVE
Digitalis purpurea

WITH FLOWERS OF PINK, purple and occasionally white, the lofty foxglove is quick to grow in cleared or disturbed areas where sunlight is suddenly available. It takes two years for a foxglove to complete its life cycle – in the first year it grows leaves and roots, and in the second year a tall stem bearing flowers.

All parts of a foxglove are highly poisonous, especially the leaves. These contain a substance called digoxin which, in tiny amounts, is used to produce a medicine to help people with heart disease. If too many leaves are eaten, they can cause sickness and even death.

FLOWERS
Standing tall like woodland soldiers, the foxglove may have 80 flowers, with the ones at the base opening first. This helps the plants stay visible to insects even as other vegetation grows up around them.

POLLINATION
Insects, especially bumblebees, land on the lip of the flower and follow the spots leading inside to the nectar. As they do so, pollen grains stick to their bodies, and these are carried to the next flower where pollination occurs.

SEEDS
You are unlikely to see one foxglove growing on its own, for in late summer the ripe fruit capsules release thousands of seeds at a time. These lie dormant until there is enough light and warmth for them to grow.

Fruit gallery

FLOWERS FORM SEEDS after they have been pollinated – a process you can find more about on page 98. Usually, the seeds develop inside a fruit where they are protected until they are ripe and ready to be transported away to form new plants.

Wild-flower fruits may be juicy berries, dry capsules, hooked burrs or feathery parachutes. Each one is specially adapted to ensure the seeds inside have the best chance of growing away from the parent plant – a process known as dispersal.

HOGWEED

WOOD AVENS

Tiny hooks covering wood-avens seeds catch on animal fur, transporting them away to new locations.

COMMON MALLOW

Common mallow is sometimes nicknamed the cheesecake mallow owing to its doughnut-shaped fruit capsules.

LORDS-AND-LADIES

Shiny lords-and-ladies berries ripen from green to orange to red at the top of each stem, like wild flower traffic lights.

SHEPHERD'S-PURSE

Look for the heart-shaped fruit of this wild flower. When ripe, the pods split open, releasing the seeds inside.

BROOM

Flowers in the pea family, such as broom or any of the peas and beans you eat, develop long seed pods like this.

TRAVELLER'S-JOY

The long silky plumes attached to the fruit of traveller's-joy are a common sight in hedgerows in winter.

SWEET-BRIAR

The fruit of roses are known as hips. The fleshy outer case – usually red or orange – protects the seeds inside.

BRAMBLE

A collection of small berries like this is known as a drupe, which animals such as humans are fond of eating.

OPIUM POPPY

When the wind blows an opium poppy's dry ripe fruit capsule, tiny seeds are shaken through holes in the top.

Germander Speedwell
Veronica chamaedrys

Two stamens stick out from the centre of these cup-shaped flowers, like satellite dishes searching for a signal. The local names for this low-growing plant include doll's eye, cat's eye and bird's eye – referring to the flower's white centre shining out of its blue surroundings. At night and when the weather is overcast or wet, these petals close up to protect the pollen inside.

If you happen upon germander speedwell, have a look at its reddish stems. These creep along the ground before branching upwards, and have two opposite lines of hairs running down them. This strange feature is peculiar to this species of speedwell.

WILDLIFE
The rare heath fritillary butterfly lays its eggs near to germander speedwell, and the caterpillars feed on its leaves when they hatch. Pollination is done by hoverflies as long as it is fine and the petals open.

THE SPEEDWELL FAMILY
This is a large family of small flowers and includes germander, wood, spiked and marsh speedwells. Many come in shades of blue, pink or purple, with dark veins running down the petals and white spots at their centre. There are speedwells for most habitats – such as heath speedwell (on the right), which grows in dry grassy places, and thyme-leaved speedwell (on the left), which is a lover of damper habitats including lawns.

FACTFILE
FOUND: Verges, fields, lawns, hedges, woods
SIZE: Up to 20 cm
FLOWERS: Mar to Jul
PETALS: 4
SHAPE: Creeping plant with clusters of flowers
FAMILY: Speedwell

GORSE
Ulex europaeus

ON SUNNY DAYS ON HEATHLANDS, the coconut-sweet smell of gorse fills the air. Attracted by the scent and the bright yellow colour, bees push their heads into the flowers, parting the petals in search of pollen. Once it is gathered, the bees move on, but the ravaged flowers remain (they are rarely visited twice). Brown pods then form which explode with a pop to release their seeds.

It is not hard to imagine why this shrub makes a fearsome hedge. The dense dark-green gorse thorns are types of leaves. In days gone by, they would be crushed and fed to cattle, especially in the winter when other food was scarce.

BROOM
When you see a shrubby mass of yellow flowers in spring, it could be gorse or broom (shown below). Check the plant for thorns – broom has none and gorse is covered in them. Broom also smells of vanilla and has long, green, ridged stems.

WILDLIFE
Reptiles, such as this common lizard, like to bask in the sun on open heaths, but they need protection from predators such as birds. Dense tangled gorse bushes are ideal places in which to take cover.

FLOWERING
There is a saying that goes, "When gorse is out of fashion, kissing is out of season." As there are three gorse species that flower at different times of the year, gorse never stops flowering – and lovers never stop kissing.

FACTFILE
FOUND: Heaths
SIZE: Up to 2 m
FLOWERS: All year round, best in April
PETALS: 5
SHAPE: Spiny spreading shrub
FAMILY: Pea

Greater Stitchwort
Stellaria holostea

CARPETS OF SNOWY-WHITE flowers appear along woodland paths and shady hedgerows from March through to June. No hint of their arrival is given, for the leaves look like blades of grass and the buds are hardly noticeable. Once they are in bloom, though, they are hard to miss – but be careful where you tread, for the stalks are so slight that it takes the lightest touch to break them.

When they have been pollinated, a gooseberry-green egg-shaped fruit capsule develops in the centre of each flower. Treading on them when they are ripe can be fun, for it causes the capsules to explode and pop loudly, scattering the seeds in the process.

LESSER STITCHWORT
As its name suggests, this plant is smaller and more delicate than greater stitchwort, and it is found in sunnier sites. While greater-stitchwort petals are notched, those of lesser stitchwort are almost entirely cleft in two.

STICKY MOUSE-EAR
It is easy to miss this low-growing stitchwort relation, even though it blooms from April right through to September. It has notched petals like greater stitchwort, but the flowers are smaller and it has sticky hairs covering its leaves.

WOOD WHITES
Delicate wood-white butterflies slowly flutter between spring nectar sources such as greater stitchwort, common bird's-foot-trefoil and bugle. They also use the flowers as places to roost on cloudy or wet days.

FACTFILE
FOUND: Open woods, hedgerows, field edges
SIZE: Up to 60 cm
FLOWERS: Apr to Jun
PETALS: 5
SHAPE: Flower clusters in sprawling masses
FAMILY: Carnation

FACTFILE
FOUND: Dry grassy banks, heaths, verges
SIZE: Up to 50 cm
FLOWERS: Jul to Sep
PETALS: 5 fused
SHAPE: Delicate flowers on thin stalks
FAMILY: Bellflower

HAREBELL
Campanula rotundifolia

SPRING SEES THE WORLD lit up with wild flowers. All too soon, this riot of activity seems to slow, and by summer the land looks dryer and less colourful. This is when the graceful blue or purple heads of harebells peep through the thin grass lining the sides of lanes, dry stone walls and footpaths.

The scientific name *Campanula rotundifolia* means "little bell with round leaves" in Latin. Only the leaves at the base of the plant are round, and these are hard to see and have usually died back by the time the plant is in flower. When young and fresh, they can be eaten raw in salads or used to make a soothing balm.

FLOWERS

The nodding heads of harebells hang from slender stems singly or in loose clusters – five fused petals form the papery bells, with five narrow, short, green sepals behind them. The sequence below shows a harebell bud coming into bloom.

SPREADING BELLFLOWER

Most harebells are purple, but you may find pink or white flowers as well. Spreading bellflowers are similar to harebells, as shown here, and have the same range of colours, but the flowers are wider and more star-shaped.

INTO THE WILD

Flowers do not recognise boundaries, and some of those planted in gardens may spread elsewhere. This harebell relation called trailing bellflower is one that has done this, and may be found in walls near to human habitation.

HEDGE BINDWEED
Calystegia sepium

THE BRIGHT WHITE funnel-shaped flowers and fresh green triangular leaves of hedge bindweed are a common sight over the summer. You are just as likely to see them scrambling over a town wall as sprawling through countryside hedgerows.

A game called granny pop out of bed involves making bindweed flowers jump out of their casings by pinching the leaves at the base. Although it is wrong to pick wild flowers in general, hedge bindweed can be a menace to get rid of and this activity is unlikely to threaten the survival of the species, for it only takes a fragment of its white root to form new plants.

WHICH WAY?
Tendrils start to appear in March when the plant begins its journey upwards, twining around and often smothering any plant in its way. Look carefully and you will see that it always spirals anticlockwise.

POLLINATORS
During the day, pollinators such as hoverflies (below), bees and butterflies visit the flowers in search of nectar. Most bindweeds close up at night, but hedge bindweed stays open on moonlit nights, and its reward is to be pollinated by moths.

FIELD BINDWEED
These pink and white candy stripes could belong to either field or hedge bindweed. This is field bindweed, which has smaller flowers and a strong scent, whereas hedge bindweed has no scent at all.

FACTFILE

FOUND: Hedges, scrub, woods, ditches
SIZE: Up to 3 m
FLOWERS: Jul to Sept
PETALS: 5 fused
SHAPE: Climbing plant with large flowers
FAMILY: Bindweed

HERB-ROBERT
Geranium robertianum

ONE NICKNAME for this pretty, but not always popular, wild flower is Stinky Bob, for the foliage smells really unpleasant when crushed. Some say that it resembles burning tyres, others say damp mice. It may be a way to put off animals that want to eat the leaves. The smell has a use, for the pungent liquid made from boiling the plant acts as an insect repellent.

Herb-Robert is sometimes seen as an invasive wild flower and can be tricky to get rid of. Even though it is easy to pull up by the roots, it has a habit of resurfacing the following year. A hairless, low-growing type of herb-Robert is found on beaches.

FRUIT
When the petals fall, a long spike holding the seeds emerges from the centre. If you gather these spikes when they are ripe and lay them out, you can watch them snap open. This action shoots the seeds out into the surrounding soil.

LEAVES
This is a hairy plant with branched stems and divided, fern-like leaves. Each leaf has between three and five leaflets. These are green at first and gradually become redder as the plant ages, or when it becomes stressed in drought or cold weather conditions.

NECTAR
Herb-Robert is an important source of nectar for insects, especially in woodlands before the canopy closes over. This female orange-tip is reaching into the nectaries at the base of the flower using its tube-like tongue.

FACTFILE
FOUND: Shady banks, woods, walls, shingle
SIZE: Up to 50 cm
FLOWERS: Apr to Sep
PETALS: 5
SHAPE: Straggly and low, with small flowers
FAMILY: Geranium

HERB GALLERY

PLANTS ARE USEFUL in many ways – for decoration, for making and dyeing clothes, for eating, and for making into drinks. The plants whose flowers, stems, leaves or roots are used for cooking or for medicines are generally called herbs, and many of them have been used by humans for thousands of years. These are just a handful of the ones you may come across.

Finding out which plants are edible and which ones are medicinal can be a dangerous business, and the journey is far from over. Much of what we know today is thanks to a 17th-century scientist called Nicholas Culpeper. He wrote the first complete herbal – a book of remarkable plants and their uses – with the aim of making medicine available to everyone.

WILD THYME

Low-growing thyme is a member of the mint family and is good for flavouring food and as a remedy for headaches.

WILD MARJORAM

Try drinking marjoram tea to cure a sore throat or an upset tummy. This is the same species as the popular herb oregano.

ROUND-LEAVED MINT

There are several types of wild mint. Use round-leaved mint to make jellies and tea, or crush it to relieve stings.

BORAGE

Borage is wonderful for attracting insects to your garden. The blue flowers can be added to salads and ice cubes.

TANSY

You could try rubbing tansy into your pet's fur to keep fleas away, or hanging up bunches to repel ants and mice.

CHICORY

The leaves are edible but chicory is best known for its roots. These can be ground and roasted to make a type of coffee.

SELFHEAL

Selfheal contains chemicals called tannins which help to reduce swellings and to dry out wounds and sores.

SALAD BURNET

This plant flowers from May to August and its young leaves are, as the name suggests, a tasty addition to salads.

WOOD SAGE

Wood sage is said to cure a range of medical problems, but it is also used to flavour beer as it tastes similar to hops.

Honeysuckle
Lonicera periclymenum

On warm summer evenings, the sweet scent of honeysuckle drifts through the air. Dusk is when the flowers are at their most fragrant, drawing in pollinators such as the elephant hawk-moth. Insects need long tongues to reach the nectar at the base of the flowers. You can taste this sweetness, too, if you nibble the end of a flower and suck in the juice.

Honeysuckle flowers have been used to make jams, jellies and wine, as well as syrups for chest infections. The scientific name *Lonicera* is derived from that of the 16th-century German botanist Adam Lonicer, who studied and wrote about herbs.

A CLOSER LOOK
Unlike bindweed, honeysuckle grows in a clockwise direction. At first its stems are green and supple, but these turn woody as they grow and age. At the end of each tendril lies a cluster of flowers made up of between six and 12 trumpet-shaped blossoms. You can see if these have been pollinated, for they turn from white to a creamy yellow colour. In autumn, round fruit form in juicy red clusters and the leaves fall from the stems.

BIRDS
In spring, blue tits dine on the blackfly that feed on young honeysuckle shoots, while dunnocks and blackcaps nest among the stems. In autumn, the bright red berries – poisonous to humans – are food for blackbirds, thrushes and robins (below).

FACTFILE
FOUND: Woods and hedgerows
SIZE: Up to 6 m
FLOWERS: Jun to Oct
PETALS: 2
SHAPE: Woody climber with flower clusters
FAMILY: Honeysuckle

Insects

The first insects appeared on Earth about 330 million years ago, but it took another 200 million years for flowering plants to join them. Since then, flowers have developed the most amazing colours, shapes and sizes in order to attract insects such as butterflies, bees, beetles, moths, hoverflies and ants to them. But why?

Insects help flowers to reproduce and, in return, flowers provide food in the form of pollen and nectar, as well as nesting sites and shelter. Common bird's-foot-trefoil, for example, is a foodplant for over 100 different insect species including butterflies, moths and bugs.

It sounds like the perfect relationship – but insects have to be on their guard. A few flowers, such as sundews and butterworts, are carnivorous plants and will actually capture and eat them.

INVASIVE SPECIES

PLANTS THAT HAVE BEEN brought in from abroad, either accidentally or on purpose, are said to be non-native. A small number of these have spread out of control or have crowded out our native plants, sometimes to the point of extinction. These plants are really bad news and are called invasive species. Many of them are now illegal to plant because of the damage they cause to the environment.

Most invasive species have very successful methods of reproducing themselves, which may make them hard to eradicate. For example, a single rhododendron flower can produce around 7,000 seeds, and plants such as Japanese knotweed spread by sending out tough underground shoots.

AMERICAN SKUNK-CABBAGE

Once popular as an ornamental water plant, this is now considered a menace as it crowds out other vegetation.

RHODODENDRON

These bushes produce nasty toxic chemicals and spread through woodland, crowding out native species.

JAPANESE KNOTWEED

Not even concrete will stop this weed. It was introduced in 1825 and was first found growing in the wild in 1886.

A CLOSER LOOK at HIMALAYAN BALSAM

Upper petal

Fused lower petals

Pink or white flowers

Fruit capsule

Exploded fruit capsule

Though pretty, Himalayan balsam suppresses other wetland plants. The ripe capsules explode, shooting the seeds of this riverside plant up to seven metres.

Seeds

Bud

Flower stalk

Pointed leaves with toothed edges

Roots

IVY

Hedera helix

IN THE DARK DAYS of winter, ivy's glossy green leaves remind us of the seasons to come. It grows everywhere – snaking over the ground or making its way up any surface it finds, often with stems growing to be as thick and woody as tree trunks.

Ivy is vitally important for wildlife. In the autumn, the flowers are alive with insects, feeding on one of the last nectar sources of the year. Birds such as wrens and robins nest in among tangled ivy branches, while other birds feed on its dark berries. Small mammals often take cover and hibernate in ivy, too.

A CLOSER LOOK

If you have ever tried pulling ivy from a wall, you will know how strongly it can be attached. The climbing stems grip by sending out short roots with sticky hairs. These clamp the plant fast to its support. Only the climbing stems produce shoots with clusters of greeny-yellow flowers. The leaves on these shoots are different from those on the rest of the plant and are diamond in shape, not lobed like the ones you can see here.

HOLLY BLUES

Holly blue butterflies lay their eggs singly at the base of ivy leaves in the summer. The hungry caterpillars emerge after two weeks and eat their way to adulthood on a diet of ivy berries and leaves (if they are lucky enough to survive).

FACTFILE
FOUND: Woods, hedgerows, walls
SIZE: 30 m or more
FLOWERS: Sep to Nov
PETALS: 5
SHAPE: Fast-growing woody climber
FAMILY: Ivy

FACTFILE
FOUND: Dry grassland, verges, dunes
SIZE: Up to 80 cm
FLOWERS: Jun to Sep
PETALS: 4
SHAPE: Flower clusters on branched stems
FAMILY: Bedstraw

LADY'S BEDSTRAW
Galium verum

DRIFTS OF THESE LEMON-YELLOW flowers cloak meadows and verges throughout the summer. Sometimes the stems sprawl along the ground, while at other times they rise upwards, with clusters of sweet-scented flowers branching off at intervals.

In the days when mattresses were stuffed with plants, lady's bedstraw was a popular filling, for the dried flowers smelled of hay and were thought to repel fleas. In the kitchen, the plant has been used to curdle milk for making cheese and for colouring Double Gloucester. Most grimly, the flowers were placed under dead bodies in coffins where they became known as corpse hay.

WILDLIFE

Lady's bedstraw is pollinated by insects such as flies and beetles. At least 15 species of moth are also known to feed on this plant, including the caterpillars of this rather exotic-looking broad-bordered bee hawk-moth.

THE BEDSTRAW FAMILY

You may be familiar with the daisy, orchid and buttercup families, but you may never have heard of bedstraws. Yet this is one of the largest plant families, with around 13,500 species, and it includes one of the world's most valued crops – the coffee-bean-producing coffea tree. Closer to home, try looking out for other bedstraws, such as heath bedstraw (below left) and cleavers (below right). Cleavers has particularly hairy leaves and seeds and much fun may be had from sticking them to people's clothes.

Leaf gallery

Leaves are small powerhouses making food for the rest of the plant. They do this by using water drawn up from the roots, carbon dioxide from the air, and light energy from the sun, in order to produce sugar in the form of glucose. This process is called photosynthesis and it occurs in all green leaves.

The leaves of wild flowers come in many different shapes and sizes. They are either simple leaves with a single leaf blade (as with honeysuckle) or compound leaves made up of two or more leaflets (as with meadowsweet). They are all specially adapted to the different habitats in which they grow. Here are some of the main features to look out for.

HONEYSUCKLE
Simple, single leaf blades

MEADOWSWEET
Compound leaves made up of many leaflets

HERB-ROBERT
Leaves made up of leaflets joined at a single point

WATER-CRESS
Leaves arranged alternately on the stem

NETTLE
Leaves arranged in pairs opposite each other

CLEAVERS
Leaves clustered in whorls around the stem

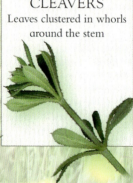

LESSER CELANDINE
Ranunculus ficaria

As early in the year as February, you may see carpets of lesser celandine covering woodland floors and riverbanks. The star-shaped, butter-yellow flowers seem to soak up the sunshine and are one of the first splashes of springtime colour.

Like many wild flowers, lesser celandine detects changes in its environment, so that the flowerheads shut up at night and when the weather is bad. This helps to protect the nectar and pollen from the cold and rain and may help to stop animals eating them. Lesser celandine often spreads to form dense mats, but in late spring it dies back, allowing other flowers to grow.

GREATER CELANDINE
Despite its name, this wild flower is not closely related to the lesser celandine and actually belongs to the poppy, not the buttercup, family. It flowers from May to August and produces long seed pods.

LEAVES
Lesser celandine's heart-shaped leaves are rich in Vitamin C and, when young, may be added to salads. But beware! Like all members of the buttercup family, it contains poisons which increase as the plant begins to flower.

WILDLIFE
Insects emerging from hibernation in early spring are desperate for food. As long as it is a fine day and the petals are open, celandines are a welcome source of nectar and pollen for insects, especially bumblebees and bees.

FACTFILE

FOUND: Riverbanks, woods, hedgerows
SIZE: Up to 25 cm
FLOWERS: Feb to Apr
PETALS: 7 to 12
SHAPE: Low-growing with upright flowers
FAMILY: Buttercup

FACTFILE
FOUND: Marshes, damp woods, ditches
SIZE: Up to 2 m
FLOWERS: Jun to Sep
PETALS: Many
SHAPE: Tall spiky stems with flower clusters
FAMILY: Daisy

MARSH THISTLE

Cirsium palustre

STANDING TALL AND ARMED with vicious-looking spikes, this plant is not instantly attractive to animals looking for food, although donkeys and goats will eat the tender young leaves. For insects, the marsh thistle is a key species, for its crowded clusters of red-purple flowers produce large quantities of nectar.

The thistle is the national flower of Scotland. The story goes that in the 13th century, Norwegian invaders took off their shoes in an effort to keep quiet and surprise sleeping soldiers. Treading on thistles caused the Norsemen to scream and wake the guard. Scotland remained safe and the thistle became its emblem.

Carline Musk	Creeping	Spear	Slender	Milk

OTHER TYPES OF THISTLE

The thistle species shown above are just some of the ones seen in the UK. They grow in grassland and can be recognised by their fearsome prickles. Only the carline thistle is not the usual pink or purple colour. Many are considered to be weeds, especially creeping thistle, which is difficult to eradicate.

THISTLEDOWN

In the autumn, marsh thistles produce long seeds with plumes of soft, white hairs known as thistledown. Goldfinches (below) and linnets balance on the spiky flowerheads as they feed on the plumed harvest. A single plant may have up to 2,000 seeds, and those not eaten by birds get transported away on the wind or attached to animals to seed elsewhere. It takes two years before new plants are able to produce flowers.

MEADOW BUTTERCUP
Ranunculus acris

THIS IS THE TALLEST member of the buttercup family. Its branching stems topped with joyful yellow flowers are found in fields throughout the UK in the spring and summer months. A double variety commonly found in gardens goes under the name of yellow batchelor's buttons.

The scientific name *ranunculus* means "little frog" in Latin, probably because frogs and meadow buttercups like to inhabit the same damp grassy places. *Acris* means "bitter taste" for the sap contains unpleasant chemicals which sometimes cause stomach upsets in grazing animals.

PETALS
Insects are attracted to UV light rays which we cannot see, but which bounce off the shiny petals. A layer of air beneath the surface of the petals helps to reflect these rays even more.

SEEDS
At the centre of each of flower lies a hard green knot where the seeds start to form. When the petals and stamens fall off, the centre swells as the seeds ripen inside.

WHAT'S THE DIFFERENCE?
In order to identify meadow and bulbous buttercup flowers, first check the sepals. Those of the bulbous buttercup (below) fold back on the stem, while the meadow buttercup's sepals hug the petals.

FACTFILE
FOUND: Fields, verges, hedgerows
SIZE: Up to 1 m
FLOWERS: Apr to Aug
PETALS: 5
SHAPE: Tall with branched stems
FAMILY: Buttercup

Meadows

This meadow seems to be full of oxeye daisies, buttercups and hawkbits, yet these are just the showy parts of a vast web of plant and animal life. To get a sense of this, try sitting down in a meadow in the spring or summer and making a note of all the species you can see, then return at dusk to watch the night-time creatures at work such as nectar-feeding moths, insect-eating bats and bat-eating owls.

Old meadows were created by farmers for haymaking and grazing cattle, but only a fraction of these remain today. The challenge is on to save this habitat, and to do this we need to increase the number of wild-flower meadows. These don't need to be large fields – you can create one in a small patch of garden by keeping the grass short in the winter and leaving it undisturbed in the spring and summer.

FACTFILE
FOUND: Damp places – ditches, fens, marshes
SIZE: Up to 1.2 m
FLOWERS: Jun to Sep
PETALS: 5 to 6
SHAPE: Tiny flower clusters on tall stems
FAMILY: Rose

Meadowsweet

Filipendula ulmaria

Wherever meadowsweet grows, there must be water nearby, for it is a plant that thrives in damp habitats. Its stiff, red stems are topped with canopies of creamy-white flowers. The individual flowers are hard to see, for long straggly stamens stick out from the centre of each one, blurring the outlines.

Life was much smellier in days gone by – before modern bathrooms and water systems were installed and when farm animals were kept nearer to houses. To improve the air over the summer, stems of the heavily scented meadowsweet were strewn onto floors, acting as a natural air-freshener.

MEDICINE
Unlike the flowers, with their sweet scent, the stems and leaves smell of antiseptic when crushed. In the 19th century, they were found to contain salicylic acid – the basis of a painkiller widely known as aspirin.

WILDLIFE
Insects are drawn to meadowsweet by its strong scent. But there's a catch, for meadowsweet is not a nectar-producing flower and so there are no sugar stores for insects to raid.

FRUIT
Meadowsweet is a member of the rose family, and its flowers and leaves are similar to those of other rose species. However, its fruits are unusual in that they resemble tiny bunches of bananas.

Parasitic Plants

The word parasite comes from Greek and means "one who eats at the table of another". In other words, parasites – in the form of animals, plants or fungi – are unwelcome guests. They live in, on or near their hosts, extracting some or all of the food and water that they need to survive. Although parasites often harm their hosts, they rarely destroy them.

Common plant parasites include mistletoe, which grows in clusters on the bark of certain trees, and yellow-rattle which you can see here. This wild flower grows in meadows, and it not only produces its own nutrients (via its green leaves), but it also sucks them up with its roots from nearby grasses. It is a plant valued by meadow-makers, for its semi-parasitic behaviour weakens grasses and so allows space for other species of wild flower to flourish.

POLLINATION

INSECTS, LIKE THIS HOVERFLY, climb over flowers looking for nectar to eat. Nectar is the sugary prize that flowers produce to attract insects. As it searches for nectar, tiny grains of pollen from the male parts of a flower, known as the anthers, stick to the insect's body. You can see some of these grains on top of the hoverfly's body.

The pollen is then transferred, via the hoverfly, to the female part of a flower, known as the stigma, in a process known as pollination. Once a flower has been pollinated, fruit can form. Other insects – butterflies, bees, moths, ants and beetles – are also vital pollinators. As well as gathering nectar, some of them collect protein-rich pollen to eat or to feed to their young.

FACTFILE
FOUND: Hedgerows, open woods, banks
SIZE: Up to 15 cm
FLOWERS: Mar to May
PETALS: 5
SHAPE: Single flowers on thin pink stalks
FAMILY: Primrose

Primrose
Primula vulgaris

As winter ends and the days start to lengthen, clumps of wrinkled green rosettes may be seen on sheltered banks and in open woods. Clusters of flower buds appear at the heart of each one before their pink stalks lengthen and the delicately scented pale flowers open. This plant is truly one of the welcome sights of spring – both for humans emerging from winter and for insects awakening from hibernation and hungry for food.

Most primrose species grow in the cool, damp, mountain regions of Asia and Europe. We have five different species in the UK, this one being the most common.

PIN OR THRUM FLOWERS
Unusually, primroses have two types of flower. Those where the female style is visible as a single dot in the centre are known as pin flowers (below). The other type have male anthers showing and are known as thrum flowers (right).

GROWING IN THE GARDEN
In the 19th century, it became popular to breed primroses. Today, they are common garden plants and are found in all colours imaginable. Usually, these cultivated varieties are less hairy and have broader leaves.

WILDLIFE
Primrose leaves are a popular meal for slugs and snails, and ants feed on the fatty seed cases. The flowers are an important pollen and nectar source for long-tongued insects. This bee-fly, for example, is using its feeding tube to suck up nectar.

RAGGED-ROBIN
Silene flos-cuculi

THE SCIENTIFIC NAME *flos-cuculi* means "flower of the cuckoo", for by the time ragged-Robin is in bloom, the cuckoo is in full song and laying its eggs in other birds' nests. This tall, pink plant thrives in damp spots but its numbers are declining, as many of the places where it grows have been drained for farming.

The flowers have no fragrance but are eye-catching enough to attract pollinators. Not all insects are welcome. To stop small insects climbing up and raiding its nectar stores, ragged-Robin stems are covered with tiny hairs. These become sticky near the flowers, which makes it doubly difficult for any hungry invaders.

WILDLIFE

These magnificent butterflies dine on the nectar of ragged-Robin flowers. British swallowtails are found in the fenlands of East Anglia, but are becoming less common owing to the loss of their wetland habitat. With climate change, we may see more continental swallowtails like these.

HOW MANY PETALS?

Ragged-Robin flowers are unmistakable for they look as though they have been cut to ribbons, hence the plant's name. Each petal is made up of two long and two short pale pink strips, which make the flowers look as if they have many more than five petals.

Red campion is a close relative of ragged-Robin and can be seen here below, on the right, and on page 106. It grows in similarly damp spots and flowers at about the same time. It, too, has five deeply divided pink petals but these are considerably neater in appearance.

FACTFILE
FOUND: Marshes, ditches, fens
SIZE: Up to 70 cm
FLOWERS: May to Jul
PETALS: 5
SHAPE: Tall stems with flower clusters
FAMILY: Carnation

FACTFILE
FOUND: Damp shady woods, banks, copses
SIZE: Up to 45 cm
FLOWERS: Apr to Jun
PETALS: 6
SHAPE: Flower clusters on leafless stems
FAMILY: Onion

Ramsons
Allium ursinum

As you walk through the woods in the spring, your nose may be hit with a strong whiff of something garlicky. If you look about you and see carpets of fresh green leaves, you will undoubtedly be looking at the plant called ramsons.

Many wild flowers are protected and picking them is against the law. However, ramsons is one of the exceptions, for it is quick to spread and it is not an at-risk species. Ramsons is also known as wild garlic and it is a favourite plant of foragers. The young leaves make deliciously pungent soups, salads and pesto and the flowers, seed pods and bulbs are all edible, too.

A CLOSER LOOK

As early as January, each narrow bulb sends up several green spears. These unfurl into broad leaves similar to those of lily-of-the-valley. If you are picking ramsons, check that the leaves smell of garlic when crushed, for those of lily-of-the-valley do not and are poisonous.

Each ramsons plant produces several flowerheads wrapped at first in papery envelopes called bracts. From these, 20 or so bright-white flowers emerge on umbrella-like stalks. The seeds form in heart-shaped capsules and they are easy to collect.

WILDLIFE

Not everyone loves the smell of ramsons, but for badgers it is a sign that food is nearby. Earthworms make up 80% of their diet, but in the spring they also forage for wild garlic and bluebell bulbs. Ramsons are pollinated mostly by bees.

RED CAMPION
Silene dioica

THESE ROSY-RED FLOWERS brighten even the dreariest day. They are a familiar sight in damp and dappled places and may be in bloom all through the spring and summer. Many wild flowers have both male and female reproductive organs, but red-campion plants produce flowers that are either all male or all female. They need insects to carry pollen from one type of flower to the other to ensure that they are pollinated and form seeds.

In folklore, red campion is supposed to guard the honey stores of fairies. In real life, it does not have many uses, except that the roots, when boiled, may be used instead of soap.

KNOW YOUR CAMPIONS

One of the plants below is a white campion, another is a red campion but with white flowers, and the third is bladder campion. Can you guess which one is which?

The way to distinguish them is to look at the calyx. This is the cup that surrounds and protects the petals. The calyx of a bladder-campion flower (left) is puffed up and has delicate purple veins; that of a white-campion flower (centre) is green; while the calyx of a red campion (right) – with either white (left) or red flowers – is red.

WILDLIFE

White campion is gently fragrant, while red campion has no scent at all. It attracts spring butterflies such as brimstones (below), as well as orange-tips and green-veined whites. Other insects in search of its nectar include bees and hoverflies.

FACTFILE
FOUND: Woods, verges, hedgerows, fields
SIZE: Up to 1.5 m
FLOWERS: Jun to Oct
PETALS: 5
SHAPE: Branched stems with flower clusters
FAMILY: Carnation

RED CLOVER
Trifolium pratense

This is one of our most common and important wild flowers. It is valued by farmers as a food crop for livestock and for its ability to improve the soil. It does this by taking a gas called nitrogen from the atmosphere and storing it in nodules in its roots; the nitrogen acts as a fertiliser for nearby plants.

Red-clover flowers are rich in nectar and protein-filled pollen, and if you grow them in your garden you will be rewarded with insects. The bumblebee below is transporting pollen grains back to its nest, carried in clumps on its legs. These are known as bee bread and may make up 30% of the bee's weight as it flies.

OTHER CLOVERS

There is hardly a grassy field or verge in the UK without some species of clover. Many clovers have quite splendid names such as hare's-foot, birds-foot, suffocated, strawberry, hedgehog, alsike and woolly clover.

Two of the most common species are white clover (left), with its creeping stems and sweet smell; and zigzag clover (right), which is easy to mistake for red clover. Zigzag flowers are the same soft purple colour, but the leaves are narrower. The other flower here (centre) is crimson clover – one of the species grown as fodder for cattle.

LUCKY CHARM

Four-leafed clovers, like this pressed one, are considered to bring good luck. This is because most clovers have three leaflets and ones with four or more are harder to find. The world record is 56 leaflets making up a single leaf.

FACTFILE
FOUND: Grassy places, waste ground
SIZE: Up to 60 cm
FLOWERS: May to Sep
PETALS: 5
SHAPE: Straggling, with branched stems
FAMILY: Pea

FACTFILE
FOUND: Disturbed ground, fields, hedges
SIZE: Up to 30 cm
FLOWERS: Mar to Oct
PETALS: 2
SHAPE: Low-growing with upright stems
FAMILY: Mint

Red dead-nettle
Lamium purpureum

Most of the wild flowers in this book are perennials, which means that they live for more than two years. However, red dead-nettles are annuals – growing from seed, flowering and dying all within a single year. They make the most of this time by being one of our longest-flowering plants.

Dead-nettle leaves look very similar to those of stinging nettles, but if you brush against them they do not cause a rash. Although they aren't related, red-dead-nettle and stinging-nettle leaves both make interesting additions to soups and salads, especially when they are young and tender.

WILDLIFE
Early in the year, bumblebees and bees are desperate for pollen and nectar. Red-dead-nettle flowers are a vital source: they are one of the first plants to bloom. Only long-tongued insects can reach the nectar which sits at the base of the flowers.

FLOWERS AND LEAVES
The heart-shaped leaves grow in pairs along the stem, becoming more red as they ascend. The flowers may be small, but their eye-catching spots and large lower lips are one big advert inviting the insect world to visit them.

WHITE DEAD-NETTLE
This larger species of dead-nettle looks even more like a stinging nettle, especially without flowers. However, if the stem is square and hairy, you are looking at a white dead-nettle. If it is round and hollow, it is a stinging nettle.

ROSEBAY WILLOWHERB
Chamerion angustifolium

IT IS HARD TO MISS these striking plants with their tall, tapered stems and hot-pink flowers. In the autumn, they become even more vibrant as their leaves turn flaming red and gold before they fall to the ground. It may be pretty, but rosebay willowherb is the playground bully – like bracken and stinging nettles, it crowds out neighbouring plants, removing any competition for nearby water and nutrients.

This plant became known as bombweed after World War II, as it was quick to grow in among the bomb-blasted ruins – in fact, it grows almost anywhere where the ground has been disturbed.

EVENING-PRIMROSE

The common evening-primrose is another tall and eye-catching member of the same willowherb family. It is wellknown for its nightly fragrance and for oil extracted from its seeds, which is used as a health supplement.

SEEDS AND LEAVES

The tangled mass below shows the exploded seed pods of rosebay willowherb. When ripe, these long pods split open from the top to release the seeds inside. Every plant produces thousands of these seeds and every seed has a hairy tuft attached to it. This clever mechanism ensures that they are carried away on the wind. If this wasn't enough to ensure its survival, it also reproduces by sending out underground stems.

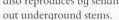

FACTFILE
FOUND: Disturbed ground, clearings
SIZE: Up to 1.5 m
FLOWERS: Jul to Sep
PETALS: 4
SHAPE: Tall single spires with many flowers
FAMILY: Willowherb

SCARLET PIMPERNEL
Lysimachia arvensis

THIS WILD FLOWER is easy to miss despite its striking orange-red colour, for it lies close to the ground and opens only between the hours of eight in the morning and three in the afternoon … if the weather is fine. The rest of the time it lies furled up like a closed umbrella, lost to view among pairs of oval leaves.

As an annual, scarlet pimpernel grows from seed each year, flowers over the summer and dies away in the autumn. Most of the plant is mildly poisonous and may cause headaches, sickness and rashes. Despite this, it has been used in the past as a cure for spots, depression and even dog bites.

A CLOSER LOOK
Scarlet pimpernels are the magicians of the wild-flower world. Not only do they seem to vanish when the weather changes, they also have to trick insects into visiting them, for unlike many flowers, scarlet pimpernel does not produce nectar to attract pollinators. Instead, tiny white and purple hairs on the male stamens are thought to lure insects into the flowers instead. Once they have been pollinated, round fruit capsules with antennae-like stalks develop, each fruit containing around 40 seeds. These can survive in the soil for years until conditions are right for them to germinate.

YELLOW PIMPERNEL
Unlike its sun-worshipping scarlet-pimpernel relation, this lemon-yellow flower thrives in damp woods and on shady banks. It is another straggly floor-creeper, but it has a shorter flowering season from May until July.

FACTFILE
FOUND: Arable fields, open ground, gardens
SIZE: Up to 15 cm
FLOWERS: May to Oct
PETALS: 5
SHAPE: Low, sprawling, with single flowers
FAMILY: Primrose

Seed dispersal

Some wild flowers grow from bulbs or underground stems, but most develop from seeds. To increase the chances of survival, the seeds are usually produced in huge quantities. If all seeds simply fell to the ground, they would have to compete with their parents for food and water. To avoid this and to help them inhabit new sites, flowers have developed clever ways to transport their offspring away. Some seeds, such as thistles, have plumes, which carry them on the wind. Others, like the poppy seeds below, are tiny and get shaken out of capsules. Hooked seeds catch on animal fur and feathers, while juicy ones get eaten and released in droppings. Most dramatic of all are seeds such as gorse, which are catapulted out of exploding capsules.

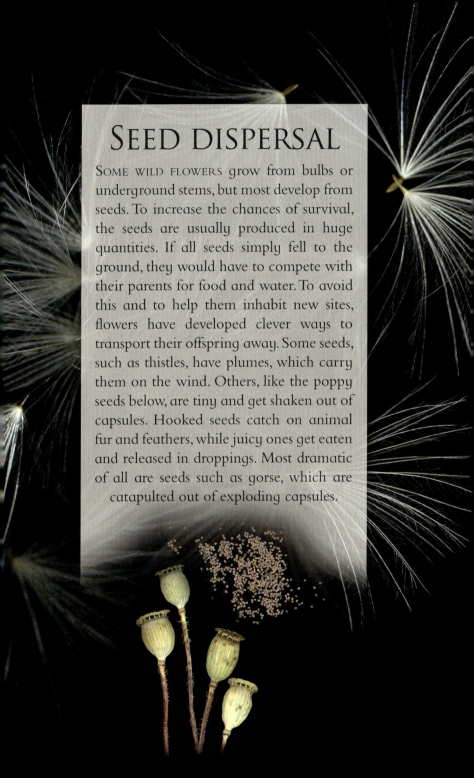

FACTFILE
FOUND: Woods, hedgerows, banks
SIZE: Up to 20 cm
FLOWERS: Jan to Mar
PETALS: 6 tepals
SHAPE: Clumps of single nodding flowers
FAMILY: Onion

Snowdrop
Galanthus nivalis

Snow may fall and winds may blow, but the delicate snowdrop is specially adapted to survive even the harshest of winters. Its tough leaf tips, or "snow piercers" as the French call them, manage to break through the hard January ground. The slender flower stalks look fragile, but they simply bend in the wind rather than break; and if snow or heavy rain falls, the nodding flowers merely sag under the weight, ready to bounce back afterwards.

Galanthus nivalis means "milkflower of the snow" and, like snow itself, great carpets may cloak the ground. Fervent lovers of snowdrops – of which there are many – are called galanthophiles.

ANTS

Oily pockets attached to snowdrop seeds make the perfect meal for young ants. The seeds get carried back to the nests by the adults, and are then discarded once their larvae have been fed. The seeds remain unharmed and lie ready to germinate when the conditions are right.

FLOWERS

When the sepals and petals of a flower look the same – as with the snowdrop – they are called tepals. The snowdrop has three white outer tepals, and three smaller notched inner ones with green stripes leading up to pollen-laden anthers. When the sun shines, the outer tepals expand and the flowers emit a honey-like scent to attract passing insects. There are not many of these around in the winter, so snowdrops tend to spread by producing more bulbs, rather than by seed.

Stinging Nettle

Urtica dioica

This is one of our best-known and possibly least-loved wild flowers. It has no pretty blooms to boast of and it is quick to deliver a painful sting to all who venture near. Not only that, it leaps in to occupy disturbed ground – especially if the soil is rich and damp – pushing out weaker plants as it spreads.

Yet nettles have been used in day-to-day life for thousands of years. Before cotton became popular, fibres from nettle stalks were spun to make rope and clothes, and pulped to make paper. The leaves alone make nutritious soups; contain compounds used in medicines; and can be soaked to create garden fertiliser.

 Butterflies   Snails Spiders   Beetles   Moths   Flies

WILDLIFE
Keep a patch of nettles in your garden and you will be rewarded with wildlife all year round. Above is a small selection of the animals that shelter, feed and lay their eggs on this formidable plant. They, in their turn, form part of complex food chains involving animals of every kind, from tiny microbes to large birds.

STINGERS
Hairs on the stems and leaves act like needles, injecting poison into your skin if you brush against them. Yet if you grasp the plant firmly, it will flatten the hairs and prevent the poison from entering you.

FLOWERS
Male and female nettle flowers grow on separate plants. Female flowers – opposite – grow in dense clusters, while male ones form long, pale green tassels, as shown below.

FACTFILE
FOUND: Waste ground, woods, hedges, fields
SIZE: Up to 1.5 m
FLOWERS: Jun to Sep
PETALS: 4
SHAPE: Patches of tall upright leafy stems
FAMILY: Nettle

TORMENTIL
Potentilla erecta

By September, most wild flowers have done their job of flowering and setting seed, and the fields and lanes are no longer awash with colour. Yet if you look down, small splashes of yellow may catch your eye. This might well be tormentil, a member of the rose family, which flowers all summer long and is still lighting up rough grassland by the early autumn.

Trying to guess the uses of wild flowers is an interesting game. Would you guess toothpaste for tormentil? Extracts from the woody roots were given to cure stomach aches, to tan leather and to flavour drinks as well as to fight gum disease.

SILVERWEED
Most members of the rose family have five petals, yet tormentil has just four, with clear notches in the tip of each. There are many tormentil look-alikes – small trailing plants with cup-shaped yellow flowers – like this silverweed.

HEATH & MOORLAND FLOWERS
Tormentil grows in both of these harsh habitats, where the soil lacks nutrients and water often drains away quickly. Most flowers of heath and moorland are low-growing to keep out of the wind, and they have clever ways of managing their food and water supplies. Sundews, for example – shown on the left – are carnivorous, and add nutrients to their diet by trapping insects. Bell heather, below right, is a wiry plant with thin leaves to prevent moisture loss and with deep roots with which to search out hidden water supplies.

FACTFILE
FOUND: Heaths, moors, rough grassy places
SIZE: Up to 30 cm
FLOWERS: May to Sep
PETALS: 4
SHAPE: Low-growing, creeping plant
FAMILY: Rose

WETLAND PLANT GALLERY

THESE PLANTS GROW in or are partly covered by water. Wetland habitats include ponds, swamps, marshes, rivers and ditches, inland waterways and areas on the coast. In some of these places, the water may be shallow and slow-flowing, while in others it may be deep and fast-moving. All these wetland areas provide crucial habitats for our plants and wildlife.

See how many of these wetland plants you can find, and make a note of any others that you come across. Many of them are aquatic versions of family members found in drier places – such as the marsh marigold, which is a big, bright, marshy buttercup – all specially adapted to growing in their watery homes.

MARSH WOUNDWORT

With orchid-like flowers and nettle-like leaves, this damp-loving plant forms dappled pink spires over the summer.

MARSH-MARIGOLD

Bright saucers of golden yellow decorate marshy meadows in the spring. The plant also goes by the name of kingcup.

WATER MINT

These pom-pom flowers line waterways from July to October. The leaves smell wonderful when crushed.

PURPLE-LOOSESTRIFE

The tall, brightly coloured spires of purple-loosestrife thrive in marshy places from summer to autumn.

WATER FORGET-ME-NOT

From May to September, clusters of blue flowers provide a sunny sight on riverbanks where insects often feed and rest.

WHITE WATER-LILY

The huge water-lily leaves and flowers rise up on long stems to float on the water. At night, the flowers close.

BOG ASPHODEL

This lover of damp, acid ground has star-shaped flowerheads which turn a golden-orange colour in the autumn.

COMMON WATER-CROWFOOT

These fried-egg-coloured buttercups grow above the water in still ponds and ditches from May to September.

AMPHIBIOUS BISTORT

Look for these long clusters of baby pink flowers both in slow-flowing waterways and on dry land.

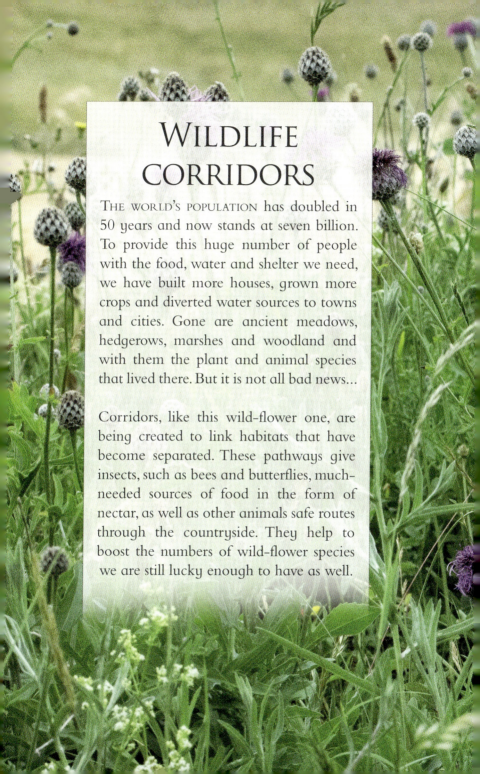

Wildlife corridors

The world's population has doubled in 50 years and now stands at seven billion. To provide this huge number of people with the food, water and shelter we need, we have built more houses, grown more crops and diverted water sources to towns and cities. Gone are ancient meadows, hedgerows, marshes and woodland and with them the plant and animal species that lived there. But it is not all bad news...

Corridors, like this wild-flower one, are being created to link habitats that have become separated. These pathways give insects, such as bees and butterflies, much-needed sources of food in the form of nectar, as well as other animals safe routes through the countryside. They help to boost the numbers of wild-flower species we are still lucky enough to have as well.

FACTFILE
FOUND: Dry banks, woods, hedgerows
SIZE: Up to 30 cm
FLOWERS: Apr to Jun
PETALS: 5 (or rarely 6)
SHAPE: Low, creeping plant with runners
FAMILY: Rose

Wild Strawberry
Fragaria vesca

THE SMALL, RED fruits of the wild strawberry are often hidden from view under its crinkled green leaves. You may smell them first, for they emit a wonderful scent and are particularly sweet to eat. Instead of pods to protect their seeds, those of the wild strawberry are tiny and yellow and cling to the outside of the red fruit, with well over 100 on each berry.

These wild flowers are easy to collect and grow at home, for the parent plant sends out long runners that sprout new leaves and roots at intervals. It was not until the 18th century that large garden varieties of strawberry were introduced.

WILDLIFE
We are not the only animals to enjoy the fruit. Other mammals, slugs and birds all dine on these sweet summer treats. The leaves are also the main food plant of the caterpillar of the grizzled skipper butterfly (below), which lays its eggs on them between May and July.

USES
You could try using wild strawberries to whiten your teeth. This involves placing a mixture of crushed berries and baking soda on them, and leaving the paste there for five minutes before rinsing it off. Repeat this once a week for a month, and see if it makes a difference.

BARREN STRAWBERRY
Looking very like its edible fruiting cousin, the barren strawberry can be identified by the large gaps between its petals. In each space sits a long, pointed green sepal, much like those of tormentil. A fruit forms, but it is hard, green and not good to eat.

WILD TEASEL
Dipsacus fullonum

THE HEDGEHOG OF THE PLANT world, wild teasel is covered with sharp spines – a clear warning to animals to stay away. Like foxgloves and most thistles, it is a type of plant called a biennial, which means it completes its life cycle in two years. In the first year it forms a leafy rosette on the ground, and in the second it sends up a tall flowering stem, which sets seed and then dies.

What is a teasel that isn't wild? It is one that has been grown for a purpose – with curved hooks on the seedhead, rather than straight spines. This plant, known as Fuller's teasel, was a popular tool for "teasing" out woollen fibres to improve and soften them.

A CLOSER LOOK

Teasel flowerheads seem to glisten with sparkledust. The dust is really white pollen coating the male anthers, which you can see sticking out of the tiny purple florets below. These open in bands, starting from the centre of the flowerhead. Insects are attracted to their nectar stores until the flowers fade and the seeds form. These then provide food for birds, such as finches, in the autumn and winter.

INSECT TRAPS

Venus's basin is another name for teasel. It is so called because pairs of leaves clasp the stems forming pockets, where water collects. Insects fall into these traps and die, and the plant then absorbs their nutrients, helping it to increase its seed production.

FACTFILE
FOUND: Rough ground, verges
SIZE: Up to 2 m
FLOWERS: Jul to Aug
PETALS: Many
SHAPE: Egg-shaped flowers on tall stems
FAMILY: Teasel

WOOD ANEMONE
Anemone nemorosa

STAR-BRIGHT, SNOWY-WHITE wood-anemone flowers rise up from a sea of green leaves in the spring. The plant spreads by setting seed and by sending out stems underground, but the roots are shallow and struggle to find enough water when it is dry.

Most deciduous woodland flowers appear early in the year, when the ground has warmed up and it is light. Once the leaves on the trees have come out, the woods become too shady for most flowers to grow. Other plants that take full advantage of the brighter spring conditions include ramsons, bluebells, primroses, common dog-violets and lesser celandines.

ANCIENT WOODLAND
Wood anemones take ages to spread, so a large colony may be a sign that you are walking in a wood that is hundreds of years old. Another indicator of ancient woodlands is the wild daffodil, which flowers from March to April.

FLOWERS
Most flowers have a ring of colourful petals protected by leafy green sepals. The wood anemone has just a single layer of white tepals. These close up at night and in bad weather, folding around and protecting the pollen on the stamens.

POLLINATION
The flower below is showing off its yellow pollen to passing insects. Below, a hoverfly lands on the stamens and starts feeding before flying to another flower. These insects are one of the main pollinators of wood anemones.

FACTFILE
FOUND: Woods, wet grassland, hedgerows
SIZE: Up to 30 cm
FLOWERS: Mar to May
PETALS: 5 to 9
SHAPE: Carpets of flowers on thin stalks
FAMILY: Buttercup

WOOD FORGET-ME-NOT
Myosotis sylvatica

THESE CHEERY BLUE FLOWERS grow in sea-like masses in spring and early summer. They are a wonderful sight, but they can be extremely hard to get rid of if they stray into your garden or even if they are grown deliberately. Each plant produces hundreds of seeds which thrive on disturbed ground, so the more you turn the soil to get rid of them, the more they grow.

Although most forget-me-not flowers are blue, look out for pink and white ones, too. In the Middle Ages, forget-me-nots were worn as symbols of love – hence their name. Like those of many borage-family species, the flowers look pretty in salads.

SCORPION GRASSES

The most common species are field, wood and water forget-me-nots. They used to be called scorpion grasses, and you will see why if you look at the water forget-me-not picture below: the top of the stem is curled up like a scorpion's tail. As the flowers open and the fruit begin to develop, the stems slowly lengthen and straighten.

MOUSE'S EARS

The scientific name *Myosotis* comes from the Greek meaning "mouse's ear" and refers to the shape and furry surface of the leaves. *Sylvatica* is Latin for "in the forest", distinguishing this species from field or water forget-me-nots.

FACTFILE
FOUND: Woods, shady banks and hedgerows
SIZE: Up to 50 cm
FLOWERS: Apr to Jul
PETALS: 5
SHAPE: Flower clusters on branching stems
FAMILY: Borage

FACTFILE
FOUND: Grassland, banks, hedgerows
SIZE: Up to 80 cm
FLOWERS: Jun to Oct
PETALS: Many
SHAPE: Flower clusters on upright stems
FAMILY: Daisy

YARROW
Achillea millefolium

Yarrow's cream, white or pink flowerheads are easy to spot on dry grassland, especially in September and October when there are few other wild flowers around. Yarrow spreads by sending out side shoots called rhizomes from which new plants develop. Cattle will eat young stems, but will bypass tough, older ones.

The Greek hero Achilles is said to have used crushed yarrow to heal his soldiers' wounds – hence the *Achillea* part of yarrow's scientific name. Yarrow is an important medicinal plant and it helps to stop bleeding and reduce inflammation, although it may not, as some have claimed, bestow the gift of prophecy.

WILDLIFE

Beetles and flies find it hard to resist a smelly plant and yarrow is no exception. Here, a spotted longhorn beetle climbs over the scented flowers as pollen from the stamens brushes onto its body. Butterflies and bees also feed on yarrow's nectar supplies.

A CLOSER LOOK

On the left below, the egg-shaped yarrow buds are in the process of opening. Together, they form dense domed heads which appear to be a collection of small daisy-like flowers. Yet if you look closely, you will see that each one of these is a mass of smaller florets.

It is easy to see why the other part of yarrow's scientific name is *millefolium*, which means "a thousand leaves". Try crushing these feathery fronds in your fingers and see if you like the scent.

FACTFILE
FOUND: River edges, ponds, ditches, fens
SIZE: Up to 1.5 m
FLOWERS: May to Jul
PETALS: 3
SHAPE: Large flowers on tall branched stems
FAMILY: Iris

Yellow Iris
Iris pseudacorus

Tall, upright irises stand like troops of soldiers guarding the water's edge, wielding their leaves like pointed swords and waving their yellow flag flowers. These impressive plants have no scent, for the blousy lemon blooms are enough to attract even the most visually challenged insects.

In Greek mythology, Iris was the goddess of the rainbow and the flowers of this family, which bears her name, come in as many colours. The yellow iris grows where water and land meet at the edges of waterways, and they are far more common than the stinking iris, our only other wild species.

DRAGONFLIES
Look for the dried outer casings of dragonflies attached to yellow iris leaves. The dragonfly larvae crawl up from the murky water below, waiting for their backs to split open and their adult forms to emerge.

BULRUSH
This is another tall waterside plant with sword-shaped leaves, yet its flowers could not be more different. The fat, dark column is made up of female flowers topped with a long, thin spike of male ones.

SEEDS
Yellow-iris seed pods are large and turn from green to brown as they ripen. Inside them, six rows of chocolate-coloured seeds wait to be released and will then float downstream to form new colonies.

GLOSSARY

ANNUAL
A plant that completes its life-cycle in one year.

ANTHER
The male part of a flower that produces pollen.

BIENNIAL
A plant that completes its life-cycle in two years.

BOTANIST
A scientist or enthusiast who studies plants.

BRACT
A leaf-like structure at the base of a flower which often protects the bud.

BULB
A swollen underground stem storing a young plant shoot.

BURR
A fruit or seed covered with small hooks or teeth.

CALYX
The usually green outer ring or whorl of sepals on a flower.

CARPEL
The female parts of a flower.

CHLOROPHYLL
A green substance found in plants which helps to convert energy from sunlight into food.

COLUMN
The fused male and female parts of orchid flowers.

COMPOSITE
A flower composed of many flowers or florets.

COMPOUND LEAF
A leaf divided into smaller leaflets.

COROLLA
The collective name for all the petals.

CULTIVATION
Breeding a plant deliberately to enhance certain characteristics.

FERTILISATION
The fusion of a male pollen grain with a female ovule to form a seed.

FERTILISER
A substance added to the soil to help plants grow.

FILAMENT
The stalk of a stamen that holds the anther.

FLORET
One of a group of flowers forming a composite flowerhead.

FOLIAGE
The leaves of a plant.

GERMINATION
The development of a plant from a seed.

HABITAT
A particular enviroment in which a plant grows.

HERB
A plant used for cooking and for medicines.

HERBAL
A book describing the uses of plants, mainly in cooking and medicines.

HIP
The fleshy fruit of the rose family containing many seeds.

HYBRID
The offspring of plants of two different species.

INFLORESCENCE
A group of flowers on a stem.

INVASIVE SPECIES
A plant that has been introduced to a new location and causes harm.

KEEL
The fused lower petals on a pea-like flower.

LABELLUM
The lower petal forming a lip in orchids.

LEAF
The part of a plant where its food is manufactured.

LEAFLET
One of several leaf-like parts making up a compound leaf.

NATIVE PLANT
One that has long existed and was not introduced by humans.

NECTAR
A sweet liquid produced by insect-pollinated flowers.

NECTARY
The nectar-producing part of a flower.

NUTRIENTS
Substances taken in by plants for growth and metabolism.

OVARY
A flower's female organ where seeds develop when fertilised.

PARASITIC PLANT
One that draws all or part of its food and water from another plant.

PEDICEL
A flower stalk.

PERENNIAL
A plant that lives for more than two years.

PETAL
A modified leaf that forms a flower, usually brightly coloured.

PETIOLE
A leaf stalk.

PHOTOSYNTHESIS
The process by which plants use light, water and gases to make food.

POLLEN
Fine grains produced by male flowers in order to fertilise female ones.

POLLINATION
The transfer of pollen from male to female flowers so that seeds can form.

POLLINATOR
An animal that moves pollen from the male to the female part of a flower.

RECEPTACLE
The top of a stalk from which a flower emerges.

RHIZOME
A creeping underground stem.

ROOT
The part of a plant that anchors it below ground and seeks out water and minerals.

SAP
The energy-giving liquid flowing through plants, made up of water, sugars and minerals.

SEED
A fertilised ovule capable of developing into a plant.

SEED CAPSULE
A dry fruit usually containing many seeds.

SEPAL
A modified leaf that protects and supports the petals.

SESSILE LEAF
One attached directly to a stem, without a stalk.

SHRUB
A woody plant with many stems, smaller than a tree.

SIMPLE LEAF
A leaf made up of one undivided surface, though its edges may be wavy or jagged.

SPECIES
A group of organisms, such as plants and animals, that share the same characteristics and can reproduce with one another.

SPUR
A tube-like extension at the back of some flowers where nectar is stored.

STAMEN
A flower's male reproductive organ composed of an anther and a filament.

STANDARD
An erect upper petal, such as those in the pea family.

STEM
The part of the plant that supports the leaves and flowers.

STIGMA
The female part of a flower that receives the male pollen.

STYLE
A stalk connecting the stigma to the ovary.

TEPAL
The name given to the petal-like parts of a flower when no distinct sepals are present.

UMBEL
An umbrella-shaped flowerhead.

INDEX

A
Achillea millefolium 136–137
adder's-tongue, small 15
Ajuga reptans 12–13
alexanders 38
alkanet, green 21
Allium ursinum 104–105
Anemone nemorosa 132–133
anemone, wood 9, 132–133
Anthriscus sylvestris 36–37
archangel, yellow 55
asparagus, family 8
asphodel, bog 125
avens, wood 58

B
balsam, family 85
  Himalayan 78
bedstraw, family 82
  heath 83
  lady's 82–83
bellflower, family 66
  spreading 67
  trailing 67
Bellis perennis 44–45
bindweed, family 69, 74
  field 68
  hedge 55, 68–69
bird's-foot-trefoil 77
  common 16–17, 64
bistort, amphibious 125
bitter-vetch 19
blackberry 10
bluebell 8–9, 105, 132
  Spanish 9
borage 73
  family 20, 21, 135
bramble 10–11, 59, 95
broom 18, 59, 62
broomrape, knapweed 25

bugle 12–13, 64
bulrush 139
burdock, lesser 48
burnet, salad 73
buttercup, bulbous 90
  family 86, 87, 90, 91, 93, 133
  meadow 90–91
butterworts 77

C
cabbage, family 42, 43
Calystegia sepium 68–69
Campanula rotundifolia 66–67
campion, bladder 106
  red 102, 106–107
  white 106
Cardamine pratensis 42–43
carnation, family 65, 103, 107
carrot, family 36, 37, 38
  wild 38
celandine, greater 86
  lesser 86–87, 132
Centaurea cyanus 34–35
Centaurea nigra 24–25
centaury, common 55
Chamerion angustifolium 112–113
chervil, rough 37
chicory 73
Cirsium palustre 88–89
cleavers 83, 84
clover, alsike 108
  bird's-foot 108
  crimson 108
  hare's-foot 108
  hedgehog 108
  red 108–109
  strawberry 108
  suffocated 108
  white 108
  woolly 108
  zigzag 108
coastal flowers 14–15

comfrey, common 20–21
cornflower 34–35
cowslip 40–41
crane's-bill, meadow 54
crocus 85
cuckooflower 42–43
Culpeper, Nicholas 72

D
Dactylorhiza fuchsii 30–31
daffodil, wild 132
daisy 44–45, 85
  family 24, 29, 35, 44, 45, 47, 48–49, 88, 136
  oxeye 49, 93
dandelion 46–47, 85
dead-nettle, red 110–111
  white 111
Digitalis purpurea 56–57
Dipsacus fullonum 130–131
dog-rose 50–51
dog-violet, common 22–23, 85, 132

E
evening-primrose 112
everlasting-pea 18

F
Filipendula ulmaria 94–95
forget-me-not, family 85
  field 134
  water 125, 134
  wood 134–135
foxglove 22, 56–57, 130
Fragaria vesca 128–129
fuchsia 34
Fuchs, Leonhart 30
fumitory, common 55

G
Galanthus nivalis 118–119
Galium verum 82–83
garlic, wild 105
geranium, family 71
Geranium robertianum 70–71
goat's-beard 22, 48
goat's-rue 18
gorse 62–63, 117
ground-elder 38
ground-ivy 12, 85
groundsel 48

H
harebell 22, 66–67
hawkbits 46, 93
heather, bell 122
Hedera helix 80–81
hedge-parsley, upright 37
hemlock 37, 39
hemp-agrimony 48
herb-Robert 70–71, 84
herbs 72–73
hogweed 37, 58
  giant 38
honesty 54
honeysuckle 74–75, 84
  family 75
horned-poppy, yellow 26
Hyacinthoides non-scripta 8–9

I
iris, family 138
  yellow 138–139
Iris pseudacorus 138–139
ivy 80–81
  family 81

K
knapweed, common 24–25
  greater 25
Knautia arvensis 52–53

142

knotweed, Japanese 78

L
lady's-tresses, autumn 32
Lamium purpureum 110–111
leaves 84–85
lily-of-the-valley 55, 105
Lonicer, Adam 74
Lonicera periclymenum 74–75
lords-and-ladies 58, 85
Lotus corniculatus 16–17
lungwort 21, 85
Lysimachia arvensis 114–115

M
mallow, common 58
marigold, corn 55
marjoram, wild 72
marsh-marigold 124
mayweed, scentless 48
meadows 92–93
meadowsweet 84, 94–95
mint, family 13, 110
round-leaved 72
water 124
mistletoe 97
mouse-ear, sticky 64
mustard, garlic 42
Myosotis sylvatica 134–135

N
nettle, family 84, 121
stinging 111, 120–121
nipplewort 48

O
onion, family 104, 118
orchid, bee 33
early-purple 32
family 31, 32–33
heath 30
pyramidal 32
oxlip, false 40

P
Papaver rhoeas 26–27

parasitic plants 25, 96–97
parsley, cow 36–37
parsnip, wild 38
pea, family 17, 18–19, 63, 109
pignut 38
pimpernel, scarlet 114–115
yellow 114
pineappleweed 48
pollination 98–99
poppy, common 26–27, 54
family 27, 34, 86, 117
opium 59
Welsh 26
Potentilla erecta 122–123
primrose 9, 40, 41, 100–101, 132
family 100, 115
Primula veris 40–41
Primula vulgaris 100–101
purple-loosestrife 125

R
ragged-Robin 102–103
ragwort, broad-leaved 28
common 28–29
fen 28
hoary 28
marsh 28
Oxford 28
ramsons 9, 104–105, 132
Ranunculus acris 90–91
Ranunculus ficaria 86–87
redshank 85
restharrow, common 18
rhododendron 78
Rosa canina 50–51
rose, family 11, 50, 94, 95, 122, 123, 128
Rubus fruticosus 10–11

S
sage, wood 73
sainfoin 18

samphire, rock 38
sanicle 38
scabious, devil's-bit 53
field 52–53
small 53
sea-blite, shrubby 15
sea-holly 38
seed dispersal 116–117
selfheal 73
Senecio jacobaea 28–29
shepherd's-purse 59
Silene dioica 106–107
Silene flos-cuculi 102–103
silverweed 85, 122
skunk-cabbage, American 78
snowdrop 118–119
speedwell, family 56, 61
germander 60–61
heath 60
marsh 60
spiked 60
thyme-leaved 60
wood 60
spotted-orchid, common 30–31
spurge, caper 85
Stellaria holostea 64–65
stitchwort, greater 64–65
lesser 64
stonecrop, biting 15
strawberry, barren 129
wild 128–129
sundews 77, 122
sweet-briar 59
Symphytum officinale 20–21

T
tansy 48, 73
Taraxacum officinale 46–47
teasel, family 52, 131
Fuller's 130
wild 130–131
thistle, carline 89
creeping 89
marsh 88–89
milk 89
musk 89
slender 89

spear 48, 89
thrift 15
thyme, wild 72
tormentil 122–123
traveller's-joy 59
Trifolium pratense 108–109

U
Ulex europaeus 62–63
umbellifer, family 37, 38
Urtica dioica 120–121

V
Veronica chamaedrys 60–61
vetch, common 18
family 18–19
kidney 18
tufted 18
vetchling, meadow 18
Viola riviniana 22–23
violet, family 23, 34
sweet 22

W
water-cress 84
water-crowfoot, common 125
water-lily, white 125
wetland plants 124–125
wildlife corridors 126–127
willowherb, family 113
rosebay 112–113
woodland, ancient 9, 132
woundwort, marsh 124

Y
yarrow 136–137
yellow-rattle 96, 97

ACKNOWLEDGEMENTS

WITH THANKS TO
Sunita Gahir – Prepress designer
Yolanta Motylinska – Production adviser
Penny Phillips – Proof reader

PICTURE CREDITS
Sea-holly (p38): Carlos Neto/Shutterstock.com
Giant hogweed (p38): Lana Elcova/Shutterstock.com
Bell heather (p122) & Barren strawberry (p129):
Martin Fowler/Shutterstock.com
False oxlip (p40), Opium poppy (p59), Primula (p101)
& Wild daffodil (p132): Alan Buckingham

**All other images © Fine Feather Press
who have spent two enjoyable years
searching for and learning about
the flowers featured in this book**

While every effort has been made to ensure the accuracy of information in this book, in no circumstances can the publisher or the authors accept any legal responsibility or liability for any loss or damage (including damage to property and/or personal injury) arising from any error in or omission from the information in this book, or from the reader's omitting to properly and accurately follow any instructions in the book.

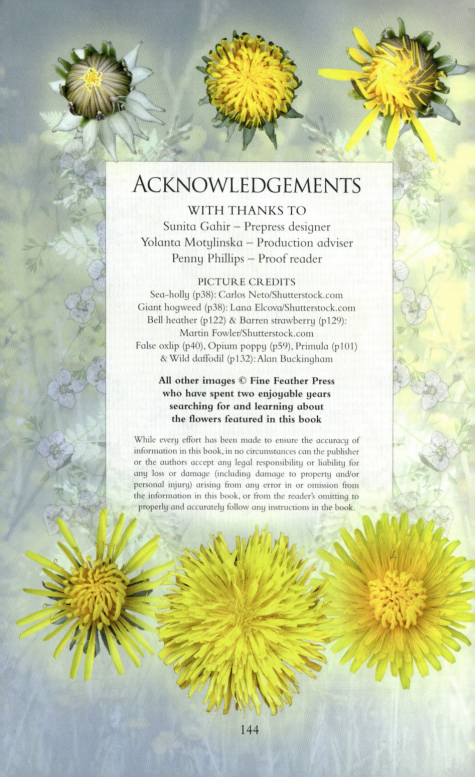

HERB-ROBERT p70	**HONEYSUCKLE**  p74	**IVY**  p80
LADY'S BEDSTRAW  p82	**LESSER CELANDINE**  p86	**MARSH THISTLE**  p88
MEADOW BUTTERCUP  p90	**MEADOWSWEET**  p94	**PRIMROSE**  p100